DATE DUE

MAR 0 9 1996	

GAYLORD   ED IN U.S.A.

D1266638

BREAKLIGHT

BREAKLIGHT

The Poetry of the Caribbean

edited and with an introduction by

Andrew Salkey

DOUBLEDAY & COMPANY, INC.
GARDEN CITY, NEW YORK
1972

First published in Great Britain 1971
by Hamish Hamilton Children's Books Ltd.

Copyright © 1971 by Andrew Salkey
Library of Congress Catalog Card Number 79-178835
Printed in the United States of America
All Rights Reserved

To
Eliot, Jason
Pat
&
Julia MacRae

It is, here,
hungry
and in the dark,
that I make everything new.

De Hombre a Muerte   Pablo Armando Fernández

He, who crosses the park, and doesn't *understand*
that blinding white light which almost repeats itself,
and he, who is, at a loss, at that time of day,
will make many unnecessary detours.

Parque Central, La Habana (3:00 pm)   Nancy Morejón

Contents

Introduction   xv

1 THE CONCEALED SPARK

Infidelities   Dennis Scott   3
Epitaph   Dennis Scott   4
Blue Sunday   Tony McNeill   5
Iris   Tony McNeill   6
Straight Seeking   Tony McNeill   8
The Early Rebels   Mervyn Morris   9
The Poets   Mervyn Morris   10
Toussaint L'Ouverture   Jan Carew   11
The Eye   Jan Carew   15
This is the dark time, my love   Martin Carter   16
Famine   Wayne Brown   17
Fisherman's Song   Wayne Brown   18
Red Hills   Wayne Brown   20
The Madwoman of Papine   Slade Hopkinson   21
Laventville   Derek Walcott   24
Upside Down Hotel   Elliott Bastien   28
Birth of a Nation   Clifford Sealy   29
Iron punts laden with cane   Milton Williams   30
Blue Gaulding   Wordsworth McAndrew   31
Child-Mother in Metamorphosis   Sebastian Clarke   32
History Makers   George Campbell   33
Jaffo, the calypsonian   Ian McDonald   34
Evening   Basil Smith   36
Poem   C. L. Herbert   37
Poem   John La Rose   38
Pain   Michael Als   39
Menagerie   Ivan Van Sertima   40
Volcano   Ivan Van Sertima   41

The Spade   Edward Brathwaite   43
South   Edward Brathwaite   46
Ogun   Edward Brathwaite   48
Colonisation in Reverse   Louise Bennett   51
A Christmas Banquet   Claude Lushington   53

2   THE HEAT OF IDENTITY
                                                                   57
Exile   Dennis Scott   59
Residue   Tony McNeill   60
Rimbaud Jingle   Tony McNeill   61
The Pond   Mervyn Morris   63
Exile   Derek Walcott   64
Poem   Derek Walcott   67
Tiger   Wayne Brown   68
Rasta Fisherman   Wayne Brown   70
My Heritage   Basil Smith   71
And Away   Basil Smith   72
Tom Tom   Basil Smith   73
Prose Poem for a Conference   John La Rose   74
Not from Here   John La Rose   76
Their Bullring   John La Rose   78
The Colonial   Syl Lowhar   79
Legend of the Carrion Crow   Wordsworth McAndrew   80
The Sun is a Shapely Fire   A. J. Seymour   82
Sun Poem XV   Wilson Harris   85
The Flaming Circle   Jagdip Maraj   86
Faded Beauty   Jagdip Maraj   87
Sugar Cane Man   Faustin Charles   88
Calypsonian   Faustin Charles   91
Song of Dry Bones   Tony Matthews   92
Blues   Tony Matthews   94
Guyanese Reflections   Gloria Escoffery   95
I come from the Nigger Yard   Martin Carter   96
Homestead   E. M. Roach   98
The Song of the Banana Man   Evan Jones   101
On the Bright Side   Arthur Raymond   104
Poem   Sebastian Clarke   105
At the Moment   Milton Williams   106
The Invisible   Rudolph Kizerman   107
Husa   Frank John   108
Hurricane   Claude Lushington   110

x

3 THE FIRE OF INVOLVEMENT   113

Homecoming   Dennis Scott   115
A Kind of Karate   Dennis Scott   117
Cub   Dennis Scott   119
The Tightrope Walker   Dennis Scott   121
Who'll see me dive?   Tony McNeill   123
Valley Prince   Mervyn Morris   125
Squid   Wayne Brown   126
Soul on Ice   Wayne Brown   128
A Dedication to Cuba   Faustin Charles   130
Soucouyant   Faustin Charles   131
Voices   Martin Carter   133
Looking at your hands   Martin Carter   134
You are Involved   Martin Carter   135
Poems of Shape and Motion   Martin Carter   136
The Intruder   Basil Smith   140
Speaking Twice   Emmanuel Jean-Baptiste   141
Poem   H. D. Carberry   142
No Joke   Frank John   143
Variation   Samuel Selvon   145
One Flower   Michael Abdul Malik   146
A Pound of Flesh at Market Price   Claude Lushington   147
Eleventh Hour   Claude Lushington   148

4 THE BLAZE OF THE STRUGGLE   149

Squatter's Rites   Dennis Scott   151
Uncle Time   Dennis Scott   153
Ode to Brother Joe   Tony McNeill   154
1–2   Tony McNeill   156
Saint Ras   Tony McNeill   158
Mariners   Mervyn Morris   160
Devilfish   Wayne Brown   161
Death of a Comrade   Martin Carter   163
Cartman of Dayclean   Martin Carter   165
I clench my fist   Martin Carter   166
On the Fourth Night of Hunger Strike   Martin Carter   167
Poem   Frank John   168
Poem   Edward Brathwaite   169
For Denis who was a Drum   Marina Maxwell   172
This Land   Basil Smith   175
Suicide?   Judy Miles   178

Pray for Rain   Milton Williams   180
Che   Derek Walcott   182
Negatives   Derek Walcott   183
A Revolutionary Core : Che Guevara   Arthur Raymond   184
Sugar Cane   Faustin Charles   185
Haunted Caudillo   Faustin Charles   187
Ten Years: 1959–1969   Jan Carew   189
Simon : How many Bolivars?   Claude Lushington   194

5 BREAKLIGHT   197

Breaklight   Knolly S. La Fortune   199
Fisherman   Dennis Scott   201
Visionary   Dennis Scott   202
Cortege   Dennis Scott   203
Resurrections   Dennis Scott   205
The Crack   Tony McNeill   207
The Other Side of the Mummies   Tony McNeill   208
Spring Poem : Brown's Town   Tony McNeill   209
The Children   Tony McNeill   211
Poem   Edward Brathwaite   212
Poem   Edward Brathwaite   215
The Survey   Derek Walcott   217
Noah   Wayne Brown   218
Having Eyes that See   Mervyn Morris   221
A pretty pot of grey   Emmanuel Jean-Baptiste   222
For G. W. Gordon   Basil Smith   224
Poem   Michael Als   226
Poem   Sebastian Clarke   229
Black Hieroglyph   Tony Matthews   230
The Coming   Tony Matthews   232
Flowers   Claude Lushington   234
After Beginning   Claude Lushington   235

EPILOGUE   237

Labourer   Edward Brathwaite   239
Citadel   Edward Brathwaite   241

Biographical Notes   243
Notes   251
Acknowledgements   255
Index of Poets and Titles   258
Index of First Lines   263

Prefatory Note

I must acknowledge my debt of gratitude to Julia MacRae of Hamish Hamilton Ltd. for suggesting the idea of this Anthology, and for helping, so unobtrusively, to see it through to publication.

I am also indebted to Knolly S. La Fortune, the Trinidadian poet, for his guidance in selecting a suitable title for the book, which we took from his own poem, at my suggestion and with his generous approval.

I thank Ivan Van Sertima, the Guyanese poet and anthropologist, for his invaluable assistance in tracking down the work of Martin Carter, Wordsworth McAndrew and Milton Williams.

I also thank Vivien Hill for her excellent typing of the poems, and for her patience in dealing with the often eccentric requests of the editor and some of the poets, concerning the matter of punctuation, lay-out and over-all presentation.

And a special word of thanks is due to my wife for her encouragement and tacit understanding throughout the editing of the manuscript.

A. S.

Introduction

After an editor has compiled an Anthology of poetry, as naturally committed as this one, which is as much an expression of the quality and momentum of modern verse as it is a sustained metaphor of the mood of his time, he ought to be able to say, 'Yes. This is where I am.' He should feel himself urged to do so, because that is the only clear response he can make to the concerted declaration of the voices of the poets, who are, in effect, the unsung vanguard of their society. I, therefore, say, looking back on the startling images, listening, once again, to the thrusting music, and nodding, in wonder, at the immediacy of the visions revealed, 'Yes. This is where I am.' In fact, I do go on to say, 'I am, indeed, at a point of departure. I have been led away from the old ground, into an area in which it is possible to create a different interpretation of our dreams, decisions and actions.'

Sameness may be dull but reassuring. Difference is usually difficult. Its acceptance does not always come easily. What is obvious, at any rate, is that something familiar has been abandoned, and something strange and bright, a sharp light slicing its way through the Caribbean, is being grasped, and shaped with inventiveness and daring by a few poets there, and by a mere handful living in voluntary exile in London.

In the work of poets like Edward Brathwaite, Tony McNeill, Wayne Brown, Judy Miles, Tony Matthews, Basil Smith, John La Rose and many of the younger poets in this Anthology, there is the textual evidence that there has been, for some time, and still is, a radical movement away from the more usual received tradition of English verse, and that there is, now, not so much a corporate

Caribbean 'voice' as differing voices from the Caribbean, through which true native concerns, intimately felt by the poets and reflected in their society, may be expressed, with broader human implications, far outside the Area. Universality has come out of a regional poetry which has, at long last, owned up to its locality and rich cultural origins. The old models, 'Euro-centred', metropolitan and approved at a chilling distance, are ignored, more and more. Those from the United States of America linger a little longer, possibly, because their influence is nearer, younger, brighter and enticing to the spirit and contemporary social preoccupations of some of the poets in the Caribbean. Dissimilar life-styles tend to have facets that resemble and coincide, at certain points, in their respective historical contexts. In the Caribbean, the life-style is a restless, anarchic amalgam of Anglo-American affinities which are often contradictory, confusing and unproductive, in the extreme. Yet, least so, is the urgency of the new social awareness of the finest of the Black American voices, filtering through the poems of Frank John, Dennis Scott, Arthur Raymond and Sebastian Clarke. Even a poet so conscious of the elegance of the Great Tradition, outside the Caribbean, as Mervyn Morris, and someone who is not vulnerable to the persuasive American cultural penetration into his hemisphere, is able to write:

> But straight is not the way; my world
> don' go so; that is lie.
> Oonu gimme back me trombone, man:
> i's time to blow me mind.

Not only has the provincial mind been 'blown' open to the neighbouring concerns in Black America, as in 'The Invisible' by Rudolph Kizerman, and in 'Poem', a fragment from 'The Gulf' Part 3, taken from *The Gulf and Other Poems* by Derek Walcott, and to those concerns in Cuba and Latin America, as in 'A Dedication to Cuba' by Faustin Charles, 'Ten Years: 1959–1969' and 'Toussaint L'Ouverture' by Jan Carew, and in 'Simon: How many Bolivars?' by Claude Lushington, but, generally, there has also

xvi

been a turning away from the trite lyricism, and aimless, decorative and derivative borrowings from the 'School Anthology' models, and from the banality of the forced nationalistic poetry of the late Thirties and middle Forties in the Caribbean.

Africa, too, has been 'blown in' from the cold, into the warm considerations of pertinent poems like 'Child-Mother in Metamorphosis' by Sebastian Clarke, 'Negatives' by Derek Walcott, 'My Heritage' and 'Tom Tom' by Basil Smith, and in 'Poem', a fragment from 'The New Ships', taken from *Masks* by Edward Brathwaite.

A truly sensitive and compassionate awareness of people, place and history, in our spiritually-fragmented Caribbean, is a very difficult level of consciousness for most of us to achieve; it almost seems a treasure, set securely in our midst yet utterly out of our reach. Surely, our poets may be the first to discover how to identify, anew, that awareness, and give it back to us. Certain signals of this forthcoming 'gift' may be heard in 'Husa' by Frank John, 'The Flaming Circle' by Jagdip Maraj, 'Soucouyant' by Faustin Charles, 'Residue' by Tony McNeill, 'Squid' by Wayne Brown, and in 'Poem', a fragment from 'Time remembering' by John La Rose, in this Anthology, and in the publication, in 1967, 1968 and 1969, respectively, of *Rights of Passage*, *Masks* and *Islands*, the trilogy of long poems by Edward Brathwaite.

The Caribbean poet's intention to reclaim the lost awareness, mentioned earlier, is reported in these lines from the Anthology extract of John La Rose's 'Time remembering':

> *I am the well-tree,*
> *digging deep,*
> *to excavate myself*
> *from within a breadth of burial*
> *that awakes with me,*
> *and plies the seas of memory*
> *and forgetting.*

The need for a radical reclamation of the spirit is endemic throughout Caribbean society. Wayne Brown states the Area's abject loss and its insistent primeval cry for the *new man*, when he says, in 'Soul on Ice':

> *I am bored*
> *with stares. What I want now*
> *are all those truths the prophets told,*
>
> *memory, infancy, where it went wrong,*
> *the ice flash, the*
> *mastodon, the mastodon!*

Indeed, the appreciation of the impact of the Edward Brathwaite trilogy, and of the urgent poems of Dennis Scott and Tony McNeill, and the call for our cultural reconstitution and political advance in the work of Michael Als, Jan Carew and Arthur Raymond are, inextricably, linked with and dependent upon our acquisition of the awareness of people, place and history in the Caribbean.

However, some years before those poems were written, we had had very definite intimations of the return of our 'missing possessions' from the signals in 'History Makers' by George Campbell, 'Poem' by H. D. Carberry, 'I come from the Nigger Yard' by Martin Carter, 'Colonisation in Reverse' by Louise Bennett, and in 'Guyanese Reflections' by Gloria Escoffery.

Oscar Lewis, the anthropologist, has pointed out that 'the brevity of possession and the singular absence of heirlooms, passed down from generation to generation, suggest that the life of the very poor is weak in tradition, and is oriented, almost exclusively, to day-to-day concerns'. In other words, our condition of underdevelopment in the Caribbean makes those who are trapped in it simple borrowers, drifters, clients of others, and people unable to sustain flights of the imagination beyond their mean existence.

Breaklight is an attempt to refute that statement, as it relates to our cultural life in the Caribbean. There is, indeed, the discovery of a new light throughout our society; and the promise, now, offered us by our young poets, is one of spiritual and social redefinition. Moreover, they are, for me, the only voices who are making sense of my own experience of life.

In our Caribbean, these poets are essentially poets of revolution, because they are poets of hope.

Andrew Salkey

1. The Concealed Spark

INFIDELITIES

Two boys battle on a flat, green field,
outside the village. At noon, when my sister
brings them thick, flaked flour-cakes
and her water-cool voice, both will yield.

There are no more dragons to fight to the death,
and young hearts are hot as the leaping sun;
that is why, and because she has smiled at one,
they shiver the gay air with their breath.

How jealous they are! How vainly they fight!
I watch the dark brown boys and laugh;
my sister is safe; when boys, at night,
in these islands, dream, their dreams are white.

Dennis Scott

EPITAPH

They hanged him on a clement morning, swung
between the falling sunlight and the women's
breathing, like a black apostrophe to pain.
All morning, while the children hushed
their hop-scotch joy and the cane kept growing,
he hung there, sweet and low.

                          At least, that's how
they tell it. It was long ago.
And what can we recall of a dead slave or two,
except that, when we punctuate our island tale,
they swing like sighs across the brutal
sentences, and anger pauses
till they pass away.

Dennis Scott

BLUE SUNDAY

Sunday evening. Memories stain
my sill. Droll figures adhere
from the desert; colourful, sheer,
they dance in from the rear of the brain.

Their lines are clean, geometric.
Facsimiles leapt from frames
in museums with forgotten names,
recalled as blue and eccentric.

I'm much too long from Manhattan
to be still found out by these jinns
who stroke, in bald, accurate lines,
the odd pulsing behind my skin.

I must learn to live with these clowns,
these serious freaks who act out
my own absurdity, these touts
of fulfilment, these harlequins!

Tony McNeill

IRIS

His glass eye's in
tight
whenever it's light.

He sleeps with it out
when it's dark
and no one's about

to see the rictus
of socket.
But, once, he wakes up, it's

pressed back in quick-
ly to mask the gap.
It's mobile and plastic,

iris, stained black
to match, and looks
like the other so much

he could almost forget
which is which;
+ the sighted

one has extended
its arc
for a view almost like normal sight.

6

Nevertheless,
some point of view has been cut in
$\frac{1}{2}$, a defect,

which skids him back
daily into the past
to recall, neurotic,

the night of his youth,
in London, when the 'long-
haired bastards' smashed in the eye:

the quick, random assault
which clouded forever
the clear iris of trust.

Tony McNeill

STRAIGHT SEEKING

Many believe, one day, the ship
will drop anchor, at Freeport.
But, now, it's enough to praise
high on the *spliff*. The smoke-
blackened city wounds
optimistic divines to enter
their pipes like dreams. Tonight, Jah
rears in a hundred tenements.
Missed by my maps,
still compassed by reason,
my ship sails, coolly, between
Africa and heaven.

Tony McNeill

THE EARLY REBELS

Time and the changing passions played them tricks,
killing the shop-soiled resolutions dead.
Gone are the early angry promises
of rich men squeezed, of capitalists bled.
More adult honesties have straightened ties
and brushed the dinner-jackets clean;
maturer minds have smelt out fallacies
and redefined what thinkers mean.

Hope drives a chromium symbol, now,
and smiles a toothpaste passion to the poor,
with colder eloquence, explaining how
the young were foolish when they swore
they'd see those dunghills dank and dreary
all replaced by bright new flats:
good sense was never youthful fury
and rash young promises by brats.

'Let's drink a loyal toast to dedication:
we mean the same but youth is past;
we are the fathers of our nation,
the thinking leaders come at last.
Cheers for the faith of simple minds!
Cheers for the love of humble friends!
Love does not alter when it finds
that we have redefined its ends.'

Mervyn Morris

THE POETS

When unseen strangers lounge beyond the footlights,
each with some personal demand,
they sing them passion's image, subtle rhythms,
with all the lying art they can command.

They march or dance; they conjure brighter visions,
or seem to copy squalor to a T;
dissembling is the skill their job requires,
if lies will make the blinder people see.

If, playing parts, they yet avoid the cheapness,
the false pretence, the histrionic fraud,
it's not their fault the auditorium's empty;
and other struggling actors will applaud.

Mervyn Morris

TOUSSAINT L'OUVERTURE
(*A Reverie*)

'Who is slave and who is free
when anarchy reigns?
I have been vanquished
by my own haste to change the world;
Christophe! Dessalines!
Pourquoi m'avez-vous trahit?
And now there's nothing
I can call my own but Death.

'The peaks of Jura are daggers
dipped in the venom of snakes;
the cold demented wind,
moaning in the pine trees,
sneaks underneath my window,
whispering of death and graves
and the putrid delights of maggots.

'This fortress of Joux
where I am caged
is sucking my life
into its damp walls:

' "Guard! Guard! Give me paper
to write again!"'

'I brought the sun in my blood,
and now it dies;
I must move closer to the fire,
bathe my limbs in flame.

' "Guard! Guard!" '

'I have been ordered to give you
no more paper, *mon General.*
Why do you write, and write?
The Emperor will never reply.
And yet, he asks about you
all the time
as though he were afraid.'

' "Afraid? After pushing me
to the lip of the grave?
Then he is afraid of ghosts
and phantoms
from the forest of eternal night."

'I am already dead.
But he is afraid of liberty.
The word's a speck of fire
on his tongue,
a dagger dipped in flame
and pointing at his brain.

'He would conquer the whole world
and weep
that there were no more nations
to enslave:
as Alexander, drunk and dreaming his life away,
wept into a wine-cup
and then swallowed his own tears.

'I was born a slave
but liberty is the bread of life to me.
I first discovered the liberty of my limbs,
dancing around bonfires at night,
when the wind sighed
in the limbs of wild mango and royal palm,
and wild birds fluted to the moon.
And, as I danced,
the shadows from the agile flames
striped my body like a tiger's,
and my feet inherited the wind:

'*Wind is an ancestor.*
Wind is a neighbour.
Wind is a messenger.

'Now, only footsteps echo
in the circle of my vacant days
as though ghosts of the fallen were on parade.

'Where are the melodies
of Ewe drums?
Where are the drummers
with their cotton eyes
and ivory teeth?
The smell of my earth
and the dreams of my people
are dismal echoes
in the forests of the long-forgotten.'

'I must give the sentries
orders for the night, General L'Ouverture.'

' "Then give the sentries
this password for the rest of my days:
Fear!
Say that I'm buried alive in snow
to drown an Emperor's fear." '

Outside, the ravens scrambled
their shadowed arabesques
on the white snow.
Nightfall.
The fires die.

When morning came the sunlight fell
upon a corpse.
The gaoler touched the icy face
and went away
to write the Emperor:
Toussaint L'Ouverture died last night . . .

Toussaint is dead
but liberty is alive;
the Haitian hills will trap the morning light
again
and the people will sing.

Jan Carew

THE EYE

My 'fore-day morning dream lingers,
like dew,
deep in the chalices of balsa flowers;
and in the cool evenings,
tinamous sing,
and bees click their feet like castanets.
Hoarse cocks,
heralds of death and not of dawn,
rehearse their clarion calls all night.
Death is on the verging grass,
where streets of eternity
rush past
the twisted sentinels of saman trees,
leading North.
The earth wears glaciers on a wrinkled brow,
and borealis twilights.
The Eye of Cyclops
peers at the distant sun.

Jan Carew

15

THIS IS THE DARK TIME, MY LOVE

This is the dark time, my love;
all around the land
brown beetles crawl about;
the shining sun is hidden in the sky;
red flowers bend their heads in sorrow.

This is the dark time, my love;
it is the season of oppression, dark metal,
and tears;
it is the festival of guns,
the carnival of misery;
everywhere the faces of men are strained
and anxious.

Who comes walking in the dark night time?
Whose boot of steel tramps down the slender grass?

It is the man of death, my love,
the strange invader,
watching you sleep
and aiming at your dreams.

Martin Carter

FAMINE

There was a famine on the waterfront.
Jetted oil spread sluggishly on a flat
sea, and curled slow fangs about the moorings.
At intervals, the drugged ocean heaved
its bulk against the pier with a dull thud.
Dead froth sucks back. Tin cans drift out. Half-
shred coconuts bunch and float. Upon the dock,
thick, gnarled fingers fingered abstract knots
in rotting rope. A loop slipped with a splash
from the stumped pier. A curse startled a hungry
gull to sudden flight. Out of decay, the song:

Land of Hope and Glory,
Mother of the Free . . .

The huge ship sank beyond the distant pole.
The hungry seagull settled on a crate.
There was a famine on the waterfront.

Wayne Brown

FISHERMAN'S SONG

From the jetty's crusted edge,
where a skinny, coppery child lolls
(eight years long) in khaki shorts,

the frail, smoking sea-pit of sky
capsizes slowly, as in dreams,
letting fall, in luxuries of vertigo,
blue wildernesses, like clouds.

Some fisherman's son:
swimmer, climber, diver, dreamer.

On him the horizon's hedge of clouds
is lost: lost too those unseen hedges
that keep men, like crabs, rockbound.

The iron sea is blazing like a sun,
but lighthouse, steamship, rowingboat, rock: none
dismays him with its quick
blackness on white, crackling tinfoil.

(Dissecting silhouettes is the aged's vice.
Yet, was I to blame? Could he know
that beyond this frail, idyllic bay
yawed a maimed, harpooned whale,
dragging, in circles, its whaleboat still?)

The morning climbed, white and wide.
Later, I saw his mirrored cheeks
crumple like grief in a sudden tide.

Wayne Brown

RED HILLS

Hyphen-stretched, between Mustang and mule,
the road trundles its garbage.
Who'd have thought love was so precise?

We arrive, sweating
from the long climb up,
loosen our ties and lapse

into grins. Red hillscar, red
nigger preserve,
our roses bloom whitely here.

The instamatic transfiguring glare
of T.V. sunsets, Alsatians.

Each evening, each streetlamp long,
fumbling with padlocks, we keep love in
and find no use for memory, though

the figure in the garden,
lost in weed,
bloom towards us with red eyes,

and the unmentionable dog
limp moonward like Santa,
a hole in its head,

dragging its bone.

Wayne Brown

THE MADWOMAN OF PAPINE
Two Cartoons with Captions

(1)

Four years ago,
in this knot of a village, outside the university,
she was in residence,
where a triangle of grass gathered the mountain road,
looped it once, and tossed it to Kingston,
where grampus buses, cycling students,
duppies of dust and ululations in light
vortexed around her.
Ritualist, she tried to reduce the world,
sketching her violent diagrams
against a wall of mountains which her stare made totter.
Her rhythmic ideas detonated into gestures.
She would jab her knee into the groin of the air,
fling her sharp instep at the fluttering sky,
revise perspectives with the hooks of her fingers,
and butt blood from the teeth of God.

She cooked and ate anything. But, being so often busy,
she hardly ever cooked or ate.

What of her history?
These are the latitudes of the ex-colonised,
of degradation still unmodified,
imported managers, styles in art,
second-hand subsistence of the spirit,

the habit of waste,
mayhem committed on the personality;
and everywhere the wrecked or scuttled mind.

Scholars, more brilliant than I could hope to be,
advised that if I valued poetry,
I should eschew all sociology.
Who could make anything of a pauper lunatic,
modelling one mildewed dress from year to year?
A scarecrow, just sane enough occasionally
to pick up filth and fry it on a brick,
she would then renew
the comic mime of her despair.

Clearly something was very wrong with her
as subject. Pedestrian. Too limited
for lyric literature.
I went away for four years. Then returned.

(2)
One loaf now costs what two loaves used to.
The madwoman has crossed the road,
and gone behind the shops,
nearer the university,
the light of scholars rising in the west.
She wears the same perennial dress,
now black as any graduate's gown,
but stands in placid anguish now;
she perfects her introverted trance,
with hanging arms, still feet,
chin on breast, forehead parallel
to the eroded, indifferent earth,
merely an invisible old woman,
extremist votary at an interior altar,
repeatedly rinsing along her tongue
a kind of invocation, whispered, verbless:

'O
Rass Rass Rass
in the highest.'

Slade Hopkinson

LAVENTVILLE
(*for V. S. Naipaul*)

> To find the Western Path
> Through the Gates of Wrath
> *Blake*

It huddled there
steel tinkling its blue painted metal air,
tempered in violence, like Rio's favelas,

with snaking, perilous streets whose edges fell as
its episcopal turkey-buzzards fall
from its miraculous hilltop

shrine,
down the impossible drop
to Belmont, Woodbrook, Maraval, St. Clair

that shine
like peddlers' tin trinkets in the sun.
From a harsh

shower, its gutters growled and gargled wash
past the Youth Centre, past the water catchment,
a rigid children's carousel of cement;

we climbed where lank electric
lines and tension cables linked its raw brick
hovels like a complex feud,

where the inheritors of the middle passage stewed
five to a room, still clamped below their hatch,
breeding like felonies,

whose lives revolve round prison, graveyard, church.
Below bent breadfruit trees
in the flat, coloured city, class

lay escalated into structures still,
merchant, middleman, magistrate, knight. To go downhill
from here was to ascend.

The middle passage had never guessed its end.
This is the height of poverty
for the desperate and the black;

climbing, we could look back
with widening memory
on the hot, corrugated iron sea
whose horrors we all

shared. The salt blood knew it well,
you, me, Samuel's daughter, Samuel,
and those ancestors clamped below its grate.

And climbing steeply past the wild
gutters, it shrilled
in the blood, for those who suffered, who were killed,

and who survive.
What other gift was there to give
as the godparents of his unnamed child?

Yet outside the brown annexe of the church, the
stifling odour of bay rum and talc, the particular,
neat sweetness of the crowd distressed

that sense. The black, fawning verger
his bow tie akimbo, grinning, the clown-gloved
fashionable wear of those I deeply loved

once, made me look on with hopelessness and rage
at their new, apish habits, their excess
and fear, the possessed, the self-possessed;

their perfume shrivelled to a childhood fear
of Sabbath graveyards, christenings, marriages,
that muggy, steaming, self-assuring air

of tropical Sabbath afternoons. And in
the church, eyes prickling with rage,
the children rescued from original sin

by their God-father since the middle passage,
the supercilious brown curate, who intones,

healing the guilt in these rachitic bones,
twisting my love within me like a knife,
'across the troubled waters of this life. . . .'

Which of us cares to walk
even if God wished
those retching waters where our souls were fished

for this new world? Afterwards, we talk
in whispers, close to death
among these stones planted on alien earth.

Afterwards,
the ceremony, the careful photograph
moved out of range before the patient tombs,

we dare a laugh,
ritual, desperate words,
born like these children from habitual wombs,

from lives fixed in the unalterable groove
of grinding poverty. I stand out on a balcony
and watch the sun pave its flat, golden path

across the roofs, the aerials, cranes, the tops
of fruit trees crawling downward to the city.
Something inside is laid wide like a wound,

some open passage that has cleft the brain,
some deep, amnesiac blow. We left
somewhere a life we never found,

customs and gods that are not born again,
some crib, some grill of light
clanged shut on us in bondage, and withheld

us from that world below us and beyond,
and in its swaddling cerements we're still bound.

Derek Walcott

UPSIDE DOWN HOTEL

The tourists peel off their dollars,
their straw hat from Hawaii,
and hurry
to photograph the sun
with their body.

Middle-class grads in mohair
celebrate their success
with blonde hair.
Sapodilla girls spew out their seeds
of ebony,
and straighten their roots
with alchemy.

On the one hand, a jaguar,
on the other, caviar,
buy local officials; still there's hope
to balance the payments,
bi-focal, on a tight rope,
of monthly instalments.

Elliott Bastien

BIRTH OF A NATION

Strangled in the womb,
our bloom is a jaundiced livery;
our time, twilight;
our thoughts, shadows
of a declining sun.

No poets cry (knowing no speech).
Today has not come.
Tomorrow did.

Clifford Sealy

IRON PUNTS LADEN WITH CANE

Iron punts, laden with cane,
come, gracefully,
like women,
into the harbour.

Iron punts, laden with cane,
make me see strong black
and bronze men,
labouring under the sun's vigour.

If blood,
instead of sweat,
could flow,
it would rain from their hearts;
and if ever life,
through overlabour,
surrendered its mortality of clay,
it would theirs.

Milton Williams

BLUE GAULDING

Stilts support the silent, slate-blue
shadow of patience,
spanning a channel of concentration
where death lurks as quick and clean
as the snip of a surgeon's scissors
and as noiseless
as the growth in a sprig of bamboo
or as the invisible workings of the starch factory
in a blade of zeb grass.

Swift eyes discern the shimmering, scaly
rainbow of recklessness,
streaking for the channel between life and death.
Mud churns with a vicious suddenness,
and the snip of a pair of scissors
in the silence
is the dirge of a young creek patua
who dared to try the keenness of the eyes
in a feathered watchtower
mounted on two weed-like stilts.

Wordsworth McAndrew

CHILD-MOTHER IN METAMORPHOSIS

Green leaves
are limp
in the street,
like a rational idea
discussed,
used
or abused
or whatever.

There's this half-god,
a grafted statue of Africa's deprecated history.
She stands, here,
in this silent land,
contemplating the departure of change,
a deadly metamorphosis.

Child-Mother, Africa,
good night,
and hello!

Sebastian Clarke

HISTORY MAKERS

Women stone breakers
hammers and rocks
tired child makers
haphazard frocks.
Strong thigh
rigid head
bent nigh
hard white piles
of stone
under hot sky
in the gully bed.

No smiles
no sigh
no moan.

Women child bearers
pregnant frocks
wilful toil sharers
destiny shapers
history makers
hammers and rocks.

George Campbell

JAFFO, THE CALYPSONIAN

Jaffo was a great calypsonian: a fire ate up his soul to sing and
    play calypso iron music.
Even when he was small, he made many-coloured ping-pong
    drums, and searched them for the island music,
drums of beaten oil-barrel iron, daubed in triangles with stolen
    paint from a harbour warehouse.
Now, he seized the sorrow and the bawdy farce in metal-harsh
    beat and his own thick voice.
He was not famous in the tents; he went there once, and not a
    stone clapped; and he was afraid of respectable eyes;
the white-suited or gay-shirted lines of businessmen or tourists
    muffled his deep urge;
but he went back to the Indian tailor's shop and sang well, and
    to the Chinese sweet-and-sweepstake shop and sang well,
unsponsored calypsoes; and in the s' rap lots near the Dry
    River, lit by one pitchoil lamp or two,
he would pound his ping-pong, and sing his hoarse voice out for
    ragged still-eyed men.
But, in the rum-shop, he was best; drinking the heavy sweet
    molasses rum, he was better than any other calypso man.
In front of the rows of dark red bottles, in the cane-scented
    rooms, his clogged throat rang and rang with staccato
    shouts.
Drunk, then, he was best; easier in pain from the cancer in his
    throat but holding the memory of it.
On the rough floors of the rum-shops, strewn with bottle-tops
    and silver-headed corks and broken green bottle-glass,

he was released from pain into remembered pain, and his thick
   voice rose and grated in brassy fear and fierce jokes.
His voice beat with bitterness and fun, as if he told of old
   things, hurt ancestral pride, and great slave humour.
He would get a rum, if he sang well; so perhaps there was that
   to it too.
He was always the best, though; he *was* the best; the ragged
   men said so, and the old men.
One month before he died, his voice thickened to a hard final
   silence.
The look of unsung calypsoes stared in his eyes, a terrible thing
   to watch in the rat-trap rum-shops.
When he could not stand for pain, he was taken to the public
   ward of the Colonial Hospital.
Rafeeq, the Indian man who in Marine Square watches the
   birds all day long for his God, was there also.
Later, he told about Jaffo in a long mad chant to the rum-shop
   men. They laughed at the story:
until the end, Jaffo stole spoons from the harried nurses to beat
   out rhythm on his iron bedposts.

Ian McDonald

EVENING

The Rasta sits in an island
of shade beneath the drying
Cassia tree. Smoke from
his chillum pipe
swathes Armour Heights in
a smog of ludicrous irrelevance.

There seems to be
a promise in the
whispering evening wind.
Beyond the blue walls,
it seems there is
a trumpet blowing.

The feel of dust, trickling
through his toes, as
he shifts his foot, is
a reassurance. Deep in
this hard earth he'll put down
solid foundations.

Basil Smith

POEM

Here are only the wind and two waters.
And now in a season of loneliness
the dark, wild waves of sorrow
invade the shores of the heart.
See how the wind and the rain
lunge and march grimly ahead
to tug rip smirch deflower the land
while the heart distils its sorrow

in a flurry of barren tears.
Night must fall and we do not know
what seas winds rains in unison
shall once more stir from slumber
and rush to the rape of the heart.
But loneliness from pain can fashion pearls
whose robust beauty is the surging forth
of the terrible strength of sorrow.

C. L. Herbert

POEM

(a fragment from 'Time remembering')

IX

Damn Caliban!
Damn, damn
Crusoe's accursed cannibal's lot!
I am Friday,
ancient child of Guinea,
Kofi,
surveying the wasted week
from the fifth day of creation,
weaving this late meaning
within an earlier myth
that moves me.
As a child, I knew Miss Quash.
Quashee, oh, what an easy,
friendly gentle woman!

X

I am the well-tree,
digging deep,
to excavate myself
from within a breadth of burial
that awakes with me,
and plies the seas of memory and forgetting.

John La Rose

PAIN

The pain
that tells the suffering
of Man
is the pain
that says only so much
for his grief,
exposing all his ugly torments
to the world,
and staying his ambitions,
while he bleeds.

His hurt pride,
naked flesh and nerve-ends
can't compare
with poverty's relief: the rum shop,
the court house,
or a wife to beat.

Michael Als

MENAGERIE

I live in a mammoth menagerie,
where the brutes put on human masks
and dance on the bars of their cages
in a fantastic zoo ball,
a year-long *mardi gras*,
known as the carnival of civilization.
I walk among shoed hoofs and gloved claws,
fur-shaven skins and silk-robed genitals,
where elephants stalk the city
with the gentle grace of cats,
and the growlers pad their throats with velvet,
speaking as softly as spectators in a zoo.
I walk where the monkeys walk upright,
like ramrods,
feigning a freedom from their four-footed spirits,
sporting smooth tail-less rears,
while the appendage continues
its invisible, indivisible waggle.

Ivan Van Sertima

VOLCANO

When I speak, now,
there are no urgent rumblings in my voice;
no scarlet vapour issues from my lips;
I spit no lava;
but I am a volcano,
an incandescent cone of angry flesh;
black brimstone broils within
the craters of my being.
When I speak, now,
no one can hear me;
the thunder lies too deep, too deep,
for violent cataclysm.
My heat
is nothing but a memory now.
My cry
is a terror of the long forgotten.
Time heaps high snow on my passive body
and I stand muted, with my furnace caged,
too chilled for agitation.
But mark me, well,
for I am still volcano;
I may disown my nature, my vesuvian blood;
so did my cousin Krakatoa, who,
for centuries, locked his fist within the earth,
and only shook it, when his wrath was full,
and died to rock the world.
So, mark me, well;

pray that my silence shall outlive my wrath,
for if this vomit ventures to my lips, again,
old orthodoxies, villaged on my body,
shall face the molten magma of my wrath,
submerge, and perish.

Ivan Van Sertima

THE SPADE
(a fragment from 'Rights of Passage')

Tall, with slow
dignity

(so
goes the saying

so
went the dream)

the negro
steps his way among the follies.

With well–cut wood–cut head,
with subtle tie

and fashionably
faun exterieur,

he needs no clowning
to assert himself: no boot

black smile, no warm humility:
no hanging

one-hand from his strength, playing
the black baboon.

43

He plays his own
game here and plays it

hard: and whether
gentleman or gigolo or

both, he holds himself
aloof from minor glitters

and does not wink
at mouching, long-haired well-

upholstered fillies, soft in public sweaters,
or turn distracted

head to watch the carefully
arranged and ready nylon

ladies' legs along
the boulevard. His glance

is only for *la femme
exceptionnelle :* the leading-

lady with no dissonance
in view: the rich-lipped generous

ewe, returning reconnoitre'd
stare for candid *coup*

d'oeil : the ariadne clue
that tries to trick him, trap him,

track him down and lead him
to himself, the minotaur.

44

There
he abides: himself: coursing his own

man-
oeuvres: jives calmly, merely nods

his head and keeps
his potent subterranean power

for his victim lover,
who through the artful

glance
the sacrificial

dance,
delivers him his chance.

Meanwhile he keeps
himself, asking no favours

and expecting
none: taking

his chance
among the dead-

ly follies with this
nonchalance

of shoulder and this
urbane head.

                    Edward Brathwaite

45

SOUTH

(*a fragment from 'Rights of Passage'*)

But today I recapture the islands'
bright beaches: blue mist from the ocean
rolling into the fishermen's houses.
By these shores I was born: sound of the sea
came in at my window, life heaved and breathed in me then
with the strength of that turbulent soil.

Since then I have travelled: moved far from the beaches:
sojourned in stoniest cities, walking the lands of the north
in sharp slanting sleet and the hail,
crossed countless saltless savannas and come
to this house in the forest where the shadows oppress me
and the only water is rain and the tepid taste of the river.

We who are born of the ocean can never seek solace
in rivers: their flowing runs on like our longing,
reproves us our lack of endeavour and purpose,
proves that our striving will founder on that.
We resent them this wisdom, this freedom: passing us
toiling, waiting and watching their cunning declension down to
        the sea.

But today I would join you, travelling river,
borne down the years of your patientest flowing,
past pains that would wreck us, sorrows arrest us,
hatred that washes us up on the flats;
and moving on through the plains that receive us,
processioned in tumult, come to the sea.

Bright waves splash up from the rocks to refresh us,
blue sea-shells shift in their wake
and *there* is the thatch of the fishermen's houses, the path
made of pebbles, and look!
Small urchins combing the beaches
look up from their traps to salute us:
they remember us just as we left them.
The fisherman, hawking the surf on this side
of the reef, stands up in his boat
and halloos us: a starfish lies in its pool.
And gulls, white sails slanted seaward,
fly into the limitless morning before us.

Edward Brathwaite

OGUN

(a fragment from 'Islands')

My uncle made chairs, tables, balanced doors on, dug out
coffins, smoothing the white wood out

with plane and quick sandpaper until
it shone like his short-sighted glasses.

The knuckles of his hands were sil-
vered knobs of nails hit, hurt and flat-

tened out with the blast of a heavy hammer. He was knock-
    knee'd, flat-
footed and his clip clop sandals slapped across the concrete

flooring of his little shop where canefield mulemen and a fleet
of Bedford lorry drivers dropped in to scratch themselves and
    talk.

There was no shock of wood, no beam
of light mahogany his saw teeth couldn't handle.

When shaping squares for locks, a key hole
care tapped rat tat tat upon the handle

of his humpbacked chisel. Cold
world of wood caught fire as he whittled: rectangle

48

window frames, the intersecting x of folding chairs, triangle

trellises, the donkey
box-cart in its squeaking square.

But he was poor and most days he was hungry.
Imported cabinets with mirrors, formica table

tops, spine-curving chairs made up of tubes, with hollow
steel-like bird bones that sat on rubber ploughs,

thin beds, stretched not on boards, but blue high-tensioned
    cables,
were what the world preferred.

And yet he had a block of wood that would have baffled them.
With knife and gimlet care he worked away at this on Sundays,

explored its knotted hurts, cutting his way
along its yellow whorls until his hands could feel

how it swelled and shivered, breathing air,
its weathered green burning to rings of time,

its contoured grain still tuned to roots and water.
And as he cut, he heard the creak of forests:

green lizard faces gulped, grey memories with moth
eyes watched him from their shadows, soft

liquid tendrils leaked among the flowers
and a black rigid thunder he had never heard within his hammer

came stomping up the trunks. And as he worked within his
    shattered
Sunday shop, the wood took shape: dry shuttered

eyes, slack anciently everted lips, flat
ruined face, eaten by pox, ravaged by rat

and woodworm, dry cistern mouth, cracked
gullet crying for the desert, the heavy black

enduring jaw; lost pain, lost iron;
emerging woodwork image of his anger.

Edward Brathwaite

COLONISATION IN REVERSE

Jamaicans, who have been migrating since the late 19th century (to Panama, Central America or the U.S.A.), turned in the early 1950's to Britain, where some 200,000 first generation Jamaicans now reside. Truly a paradox of colonial history is this colonisation in reverse to the Mother Country which once settled her colonies with Britons who came as planters, traders, administrators, technicians, etc.

Poet's Note

Wat a joyful news, Miss Mattie!
I feel like me heart gwine burs';
Jamaica people colonizin
Englan in reverse.

By de hundred, by de t'ousan,
from country and from town,
by de ship-load, by de plane-load,
Jamaica is Englan boun.

Dem a-pour out o'Jamaica;
everybody future plan
is fe get a big-time job
and settle in de mother lan.

What a islan! What a people!
Man an woman, old an young,
jusa pack dem bag an baggage
an tun history upside dung!

51

Some people don't like travel,
but fe show dem loyalty,
dem all a-open up cheap-fare-
to-Englan agency.

An week by week, dem shippin off
dem countryman like fire,
fe immigrate an populate
de seat o' de Empire.

Oonoo see how life is funny?
Oonoo see de tunabout?
Jamaica live fe box bread
outa English people mout'.

For wen dem catch a Englan,
an start play dem different role,
some will settle down to work
an some will settle fe de dole.

Jane say de dole is not too bad
because dey payin' she
two pounds a week fe seek a job
dat suit her dignity.

Me say Jane will never find work
at the rate how she dah-look,
for all day she stay pon Aunt Fan couch
an read love-story book.

Wat a devilment a Englan!
Dem face war an brave de worse;
but I'm wonderin' how dem gwine stan'
colonizin' in reverse.

Louise Bennett

A CHRISTMAS BANQUET

Pinned to the clothes-line of time to dry,
black Simon under Christ's cross, dressed
in a snow uniform, struck at shackles just
as Moses had done when he hammered rocks,
saw waters gush heavy with the sky's teardrops.

And so to lost horizons through a peephole
of years and vistas, backwards, today, I am
looking for poui trees and flamboyants,
frangipani and hibiscus: the soft mantillas
on the peaks of the West Indian brows. But,
I see, instead of valleys of nutmeg and clove,
sleeping quietly in white cotton beds, their
tresses like snow caps on the tops of trees
in faraway countries, another place, another time,
when, once, there came a Jew to sleep in a manger,
and, later, hang his coat on nails, in a hilltop
tree, in whose naked shade, by legend darkly
overspread, men were meant to shelter, when
fed with blood and bread, in a lost evening
of time.

In a softer clime of memory, such tender
weapons of fate were like vespers, at day's-end,
which make faces of flowers smile, and heart glad,
when making a way for love that grows in rows,
in the cornfield's shrine. But at a harsher

time of the year's cycle, the temporal image of man,
thus expressed, seeks conquest, in busy lives,
finds that sunset stands up against dawn, and
midnight pleasures refuse to recline before
afternoon: thus the chicken-noodle soup in slot
machines wishes to crow thrice, as if to deny
the whisky flowing over the caviar, the bread
standing up against the wine, in a communion larder.

So, across an ocean of time, this Christmas
day, let me listen, once more, to the waters
lapping on a West Indian shore; let me look
at the river's-edge, jagged by the definition
of dead sea, crag and precipice, once defined,
now mere declensions in time; then let me have
the homing instinct return, as kind thought:
libations at the feast of lonely men,
where sea-gulls of memory dip
tongues into the brine of my sweat to taste
the infinite in me; after which gulping
creation in oceanfuls, let them rise like brides
who escape their honeymoon, and bridegrooms who,
lying in some *de profundis*, try to ring the wedding
bells of *Te Deum*.

But, a white carnation grows,
I see, on the edge of the sea,
and it laps the waters with its petals
so that hurricanes recede.
The water is calm.
Savage birds preen their feathers in sandgroves,
while civilised men, everywhere,
must go on, still, breaking bread together
at the foot of the volcano,
drinking rum from a common urn,
crimson with blood of the centuries

which oozes still through
the belly of time, violent with friction,
and volatile with peace.

So, on this Christmas morning,
I seem to feel that I ought to remake
the shape of time, and refind the soul of Eternity,
still eating, as I do, bread baked in a volcano,
and drinking drink, bottled in agony.
But, an ice impressionism shapes the surrealism,
burning in my mind like a bedside lamp: dialectical.
I feel the power of the flower I see outside my window,
imprisoned by its stalk, and trying hard to explode
like a rocket, spilling its guts all over the earth,
when there is darkness at noon,
and when, in winter, the rose forgets to bloom.

Claude Lushington

2. The Heat of Identity

EXILE

There is a kind of loss,
like coming home
to faces; the doors open indifferently; *they* whisper,
'Who is this, with dust
in his mouth? Who
is this new traveller?
Tell us of birds,
migrating the dull sky,
half a world round,
of Ithaca, and the tiered beast,
of that foreign city
you sent your pale card from!'

There are patterns to assure us:
at table, familiar spices;
the garden, hardly greener;
but, something has changed:
clothes we left behind;
the old affections hang loosely.
Suddenly, mouth is dumb; eyes
hurt; surprised, it is we
who have changed; glad, now,
to have practised loving
before that departure. To travel
is to return
to strangers.

Dennis Scott

RESIDUE

I

The wind is crisp, and carries
a tang of the sea. The flowers
burn richly against the grass.
The grass itself shines, and is precious.

II

Ahead, the sky and the ocean
merge in a stain of blue. On the beach,
yesterday, lolloping tourists
were posting umbrellas like crosses.

III

This morning, I chose to stay home,
to watch the cats, and think of
Columbus. And the grass is precious
merely because it belongs to us.

Tony McNeill

RIMBAUD JINGLE

On Sunday, all come to the zoo.
Zipped in my ape-suit tight, I freak
public. When a child tosses a
peanut through, I eat it like you.

This is a zoo. And who are you?
Outside my cage, sane citizens
lime on stilts in their Sunday-suits.
Slinging in fruit, they make me do

an insane rock-steady for you;
make me stand on my head and do
other tricks to almost prove right
my wrong-presence here in this zoo.

This is a cage. And who are you?
Two neighbouring lions, half-seen
through slits, recline in the sun.
They hate everything human; will do

not even the least trick for you.
Their common contempt makes us one.
I pitch back your fruit. When you trip
on my skin of sickness, bruised blue,

I'll slip from my cage, and into
the pure life of lions. I am death-
sick of being two. These sane green
animals seal my rent like glue.

On Sunday, all come to the zoo.
Zipped out, it's easy to freak in
from you. But, conversely, right on
cue, the others do tricks for you.

Tony McNeill

THE POND

There was this pond in the village
and little boys, he heard till he was sick,
were not allowed too near.
Unfathomable pool, they said,
that swallowed men and animals just so;
and in its depths, old people said,
swam galliwasps and nameless horrors;
bright boys kept away.

Though drawn so hard by prohibitions,
the small boy, fixed in fear, kept off;
till one wet summer, grass growing lush,
paths muddy, slippery, he found himself
there, at the fabled edge.

The brooding pond was dark.
Sudden, escaping cloud, the sun
came bright; and, shimmering in guilt,
he saw his own face peering from the pool.

Mervyn Morris

EXILE

(a poem from 'The Gulf')

Wind-haired, mufflered
against dawn, you watched the herd
of migrants ring the deck
with silence. Only the funnel,
bellowing, the gulls who peck
waste from the ploughed channel
knew that you had not come
to England; you were home.

Even her wretched weather
was poetry. Your scarred leather
suitcase held that first
indenture, to her Word,
but, among cattle docking, that rehearsed
calm, meant to mark you from the herd,
shook, calf-like, in her cold.

Never to go home again,
for this was home! The windows
leafed through history to the beat
of a school ballad, but the train
soon changed its poetry to the prose
of narrowing, pinched eyes you could not enter,
to the gas-ring, the noisy Students' Centre,
to the soiled, icy sheet.

64

At night, near rheum-eyed windows,
your memory kept pace with winter's
pages, piled in drifts,
till Spring, which slowly lifts
the heart, saw your first pages
and suns you had forgotten
blazoned from barrows.

And earth began to look
as you remembered her;
herons, like sea-gulls, flock-
ed to the ploughed furrow;
the bellowing, black bullock
churned its cane sea;
a world began to pass
through your pen's eye,
between bent grasses and one word
for the bent rice.

And now, some phrase,
caught in the parenthesis
of highway, quietly states
its title, and an ochre trace
of flags and carat huts opens
at Chapter One;
the bullock's strenuous ease is mirrored
in a clear page of prose;
a forest is compressed in a blue coal,
or burns in graphite fire;
invisibly, your ink nourishes,
leaf after leaf, the furrowed villages,
where the smoke flutes
and the brown pages
of the Ramayana stoke the mulch fires;

the arrowing, metal
highways head elsewhere;
the tabla and the sitar amplified,
the Path unrolling like a dirty bandage,
the cinema-hoardings leer
in language half the country cannot read.

Yet, when dry winds rattle
the flags whose bamboo lances bend
to Hanuman, when, like chattel
folded in a cloth-knot, the debased
brasses are tremblingly placed
on flaking temple lintels,
when a hand shakes the bells
and smoke writhes its blue arms
for your lost India,

the old men, threshing rice,
rheum-eyed, pause,
their brown gaze flecked with chaff,
their loss chafed by the raw
whine of the cinema-van calling the countryside
to its own dark devotions,
summoning the drowned from oceans
of deep cane. The hymn
to Mother Indian whores its lie.
Your memory walks by its soft-spoken
path, as flickering, broken,
Saturday jerks past like a cheap film.

Derek Walcott

POEM

(*a fragment of 'The Gulf' Part 3 from* The Gulf)

Yet the South felt like home. Wrought balconies,
the sluggish river with its tidal drawl,
the tropic air charged with the extremities

of patience, a heat heavy with oil,
canebrakes, that legendary jazz. But fear
thickened my voice; that strange, familiar soil

prickled and barbed the texture of my hair,
my status as a secondary soul.
The Gulf, your guilt, is daily widening;

each blood-red rose warns of that coming night,
when there's no rock cleft to go hidin' in
and all the rocks catch fire, when that black might,

their stalking, moonless panthers turn from Him
whose voice they can no more believe, when the black X's
mark their passover with slain seraphim.

Derek Walcott

TIGER

The sun's no friend of mine, who grew up
around the glinting of moonlight on leaves.
All day I keep my eyes screwed tight
against the cascade of blood at my brain.
At night I come down from the trees.

No morality stalks my descent;
my logic is murder; I move on.
The dangling tail, the quiet shriek,
the fragile rustle of leaf on leaf,
the wildly staring eye:
these are offensive to me; that is all.
Memories distend my nostrils.

I am totally unexpected. I inhabit
the spaces of heights. The
moonlit deer, young boar, zebra
asleep in the grass: all
these are of prime interest to me;
these I make my business.

I am the nebulous footpad, man's
slow dance with death. I was there
just before you turned round. And
the catacombs, dark, wherein men retreat,
I constantly seek and gain access to them.

It is useless to keep me caged.
One day they will leave the gate out.
I am in constant readiness of this.
Parts of me never sleep.

Wayne Brown

RASTA FISHERMAN

Old Rasta, how that rumpled bark becomes you still
surprises me, like the moon's answer after a squall.
Once creator of silence and shade, now it's hard
put merely to survive. I know, Yacht-Owner. I

know: reluctant mariner, lost between two tides,
your moss-browed eyes hooked to a fish,
I must not raise for you
those wrecking truths your placid gaze denies.

The sun is behind you still, old man;
you ride towards your landfall.
When the time comes
beneath your barnacled feet, all earth shall be

the lion's beach, Ethiopia shining, not this
silly shifting island
of bark. I know, Yacht-Owner. I know.

Wayne Brown

MY HERITAGE

My heritage is of the night,
of dry-thatch cottages,
of painted faces,
and of drums.

My memory shows
dry mountain tops,
green fields and trees
that never grey or die.

So I stand misunderstood,
hated for the thickness of my lips
and my memories of drums.

Basil Smith

AND AWAY

I realise now that
I am not at home,
in Spring, in my terms,
in the lush terms of green
and magical colours which Nature
provides.

Sometimes,
when I'm feeling low,
I wish someone would come
and lift me away from here,
like a crane above the marshes,
a gull over a restless sea.
But I couldn't rest easy
if I were to up and leave
you behind, suffering, slaving and
doing time.

This morning when I got awake
I started carving
a brand new frontier,
here, in this wild,
wild west.

Basil Smith

TOM TOM

Give me tom-tom,
abeng, abeng, abeng!
Carve my features
in the likeness of
a bronze Yoruba mask!
Give me personality
the rhythm of the drum, and
make my blood boil
to the temperature of the Sahara!
Teach me to dance
the way my grandmother
has forgotten, and don't
hide
the face of Shango
from me.
Then,
and only then,
shall I be a *man*.

Basil Smith

73

PROSE POEM FOR A CONFERENCE

We're a people of exile, living in the permanence
of tragedy
and dispossessed hope. We are the wanderers
and a
wonder of this world. We have survived,
deprived of
pristine utterance, appropriating and welding
language out of ancestral wounds and
sacrifice.
Wounds, still fresh-cut, work under my words.
In the
colloquy of everything, everything present lives
with
everything past in momentary and im-
perfect blindness.
We are, such as we are, the living tissue of
contem-
poraneity, caught in islands, or thicker land
masses,
plying our own triangular trade in ourselves,
exporting ourselves from hopelessness into hope,
from disillusion
with anaemic illusion, avoiding the pilgrimage
of
return into the dark unmentionable habitats
that lie in
ourselves; and we have lived to fight.

Such as we are, we are the salted embryo
of a world whose fixities grow loose,
while ours, our world, once indecently
                    naked
and rootless, becomes firm, and gells for the encounter
                    with history, ready.
Fragments of roots, scorned in the night
                    of self-contempt, spring
to re-birth: the seed of renewal. Exile paid its premium
                    in self-awareness.
We begin to know: a message of hope and
                    contradiction.
But such is my message.

John La Rose

NOT FROM HERE

You were not born, here,
        my child,
        not here.

You saw daylight
among our islands;
the sun was always there.

None could tap the light
from your eyes,
or dictate roofs into space,
        for your colour.

There, in the middle of a hemisphere,
you and I were born,
        down there.

We were not in the exodus;
there was no Moses;
and this was no promised land.

You may not know this, yet,
        my son;
I sense that you sense it.

Yet, what we leave
               we carry.
It is no mud
               we dry
on our boots.

John La Rose

THEIR BULLRING

Suffering,
smiling,
singing:
these are the cadences
in the rhythms of my living.

No one knew
that I was thinking
and how I ached
when I was loving.

No one thought
that I was watching.

What they saw
was smiling,
jazzing,
bluesing.

Only my teeth:
that was the passport they accept
and wanted
for their bullring.

John La Rose

THE COLONIAL

From the hollowness of the cave,
I come, the echo of a cry
of pain, the shadow of a slave
whose sole salvation was the grave.

My bone fertilises the earth;
my blood lubricates the machine;
my sweat waters the field: my worth
was predetermined at my birth.

I carve my memory on rock;
preserve my grief in song.
I'm slammed by the racket,
like a shuttlecock,
from this to that imperial block.

Broken in spirit and in frame,
I stand on the verge of tomorrow
with the incubus of my shame,
without identity, without a name.

Syl Lowhar

LEGEND OF THE CARRION CROW

They call you Carrion Crow;
scorn to eat your flesh;
spit, when they see you administering the last rites;
and call you *Cathartes*, the 'Clean-up'.
Yet, if they only knew
the secret of your strange religion.

Once,
you were the silver bird of the heavens;
once,
you flew as high and as free
as only a bird can. The sky was yours,
for you were 'King of the Air';
but here
was the secret of your discontent: it was not enough
just to live and die, not knowing;
you kept asking, 'Where did I come from?'
'Where am I going?'
and 'Why?'

The sky must hold the answer,
you thought,
and sought long and desperately hard
to glimpse what lay beyond it.

You fought, relentlessly,
pitted bone and feather and tendon
against the blue barrier that mocked you,
locked you off
from the secret world behind its curvature.
But, you were more determined
than it knew,
and you could fly higher.

So, you sweated at your quest,
until, one inspired day, you flew
so fast against the blue,
closing your wings at the last minute
for penetration,
that, in the end, you had a look at the other side.

Nobody knows what you saw,
when you passed through,
but you burned in that sacred blue fire,
and returned, black as coal, numb,
dumb from the experience,
to become this mendicant preacher,
minister to those souls who die without sacrament,
trading blessings for food,
a saved soul for a full belly.

And, now, when I see you,
crowding a carcass for the unction,
or nailed against the sky like a crucifix,
with the two spots of tarnished silver
beneath your wings, where you had closed them,
I long to have you say a 'De Profundis' for me,
when I die;
and I wonder: was yours a punishment or a purification?

Wordsworth McAndrew

THE SUN IS A SHAPELY FIRE

The sun is a shapely fire,
turning in the air,
and fed by white springs;
and the earth is a powerless sun.

(1)

I have the sun, today, deep in my bones.
The sun is in my blood.
The light heaps beneath my skin.
The sun is a badge of power,
pouring into a darkening star
which rains down its glory.

The trees and I are cousins: those tall trees
that tier their branches in the hollow sky,
and, high up, hold small swaying hands
of leaves up to a divinity,
their name for the sun,
and, sometimes, mine: we're cousins.

The sheet light, while power
comes falling through the air
(All the light, here, is equal vertical),
plays magic with the green leaves,
and, touching them,
wakes the small sweet springs
of breathing scent and bloom

82

which break out on the boughs.
And the sun has made
civilisation flower from a river's mud
with his gossamer rays of steel.

(ii)
These regions wear sharp shadows
from the deep sun.
The sun gives back her earth
its ancient right: the gift of violence.
Life, here, is ringed
with half of the sun's wheel;
and our limbs and passions grow
in leaps of power
suddenly flowing up to touch the arc.

On this energy, kin to the sun,
we learn the trick of discipline and the slow skill
of squaring-in towns on an empty map,
of hitching rivers to great water wheels,
and of taming the fire to domesticity.

(iii)
The sun is a shapely fire
floating in the air
and watched by the eye of God.
The distance makes it cool
with the slow, circling retinue of worlds,
hanging on it.
Indifferently near,
other stars move with their attendant groups,
keeping and breaking pace,
in the afternoon,
until the enormous music fades
and dies away.

The sun is a shapely fire,
turning in the air.
The sun is in my blood.

A. J. Seymour

SUN POEM XV

Blue is the journey I long to go.
White is the gate I open
to show the sun my face.
Brown is the road that leads to space
where the sky falls down
like the highest hill.

Dark is the river
where green trees sail,
where nothing learns to stand quite still
on the visionary road across the hill.
Lofty is the spirit that waves on high
like a flag of wind that is flown awry;
it is visible now to my naked eye,
to my naked eye and my naked mind;
the flag blows out and the wind blows in;
they are one and the same
like flesh and skin.

My wood and my bone are burnt in the sun.
I wave like smoke, crackle like gun,
march to meet the starry ground,
where the camps are lit and the spirits sound
their bugles for burning bone and tongue.

Wilson Harris

THE FLAMING CIRCLE

Towards that flaming circle
first glimpsed in the heart
of my mother, I leap
with a sense of joy created
by the sad beauty of every face
that my eyes have kissed,
by the dance of words, and
the purge of thought by thought.

How far is it beyond the flaming circle
to that other world of being
known to sages who had learnt
to walk among the trees of India,
not like the snake sliding on belly,
savage beasts charging forward,
nor the civilised hunter with pointed gun,
but with eyes that searched ever upwards
for the rain that caused the Lotus to grow?

Let me soar
beyond the flaming circle,
to listen for the sound of petal on petal
and to feel the warmth of hands within my reach.

Jagdip Maraj

FADED BEAUTY

Severed by mercenary fate,
they tried to suckle a new land.

Breasts withered
like the branches of a tree
uprooted by a savage wind, and
orphaned children, when the cane's
heat had dulled their pain,
became stiff, insensitive.

The beauty of a race faded.
Today, it breathes asthmatically
in impure forms about the country
and in venal Brahmins repeating
the Scriptures with strange intensity.

Jagdip Maraj

SUGAR CANE MAN

Who am I,
black,
with my woolly, plaited hair,
my thick lips,
my rich, red blood
and my tall, muscular body?

My generation worked in the cane-fields,
its labour gone in vain,
in somebody else's service,
for somebody else's profit;
there was no gratitude, no sharing;
there was only Massa,
on his puppet throne;
his whip reminded us of our existence.

We, often, felt like running away.
But where could we go, and
who would take us in?
At night, we sang.
But why did we sing, as we did,
in such a state of mind, and
why did we bother to create new sounds?

The ideal of resistance seemed carved,
deep, inside us,
moulded by Nature, and
banked like a forest fire by rain
and damp leaves.

We had no names,
only borrowed tags,
hand-me-down misfits,
or numbers,
Massa's cast-off family features,
and always the branding iron.

We had no real beginning,
and no end in view,
only a paraphrase of cruelty
and death,
and a large cross,
our consciousness.

Our language was the drum
and the quick gesture in the dark;
at night, we harmonized,
in disguise,
a ritual and a way of life.

We killed a white rooster
against a white-washed wall;
and we watched the blood flow
along the out-house gutter.

The ones, who died, then, left us,
in the dry season,
but they went on
to become united, once more,
with their dreams;
and to those,
who lived to tell the tale, secondhand,
elsewhere,
we say that their lives
and ours
are our own epitaph,
written down, permanently,
in sugar cane,
in spite of the fragmentation of history.

Faustin Charles

CALYPSONIAN

You chime sweet sounds
in rhythm and rhyme;
music pours from the arteries
of your guitar,
composed in a flood of melody;
the inspiring tune shapes hot words,
and boldly evokes
a triumphant complex of syllables.
Agile, diamond vocals stimulate
the barn dance
of your painted vernacular;
and a cynical humming-bird
joins the jump-up
of your vanguard voice,
improvising on a prosperous chorus
the Island's Angelus.

Faustin Charles

SONG OF DRY BONES

My choir and your choir
‚ are
ten million skeletons
from the bottom of the Atlantic
up to the warm, lapping Caribbean.

The slow wind, the sob of history,
the mighty storm of the waves
and their last dying echoes
are
ten million skeletons
beating out the rhythm of dry bones.

It's the Blues
and more.

Yes, now, shake, rattle
and roll
'The Twist'
'The Watusi'
and the choir of the dead.

We dance our fleshless dance
to a bone percussion.
I am jointless in the streets.
I am rhythmical in the Caribbean.
My movements are rich
with pain,
but my agony is without flesh.

There is no name to name the sound
that echoes on the waves.
Call it the Blues;
I call it the Hymn of the Bones.

Tony Matthews

BLUES

A blues in the night
is an owl on the prowl.

A blues-singing owl
is one on a deadly prowl
singing and seeing
far into the night.

Tony Matthews

GUYANESE REFLECTIONS

Georgetown Boy

Hear me boast, *bai*, brother:
I, clay Krishna, swimming in the trench,
blue ghosting through clouds, dropped from God's
own fingers.
Dare you catch me, now, *bai!*
Upheeled Krishna,
tip top flag-pole down in *koker* temple,
splintered.

Rupununi Savannah

This sullen king caiman, foreign to my hill-trained eye,
loops the plain, shoals in rust, splays and joins ochre to umber
in a river of light;
makes emerald glow
in concentration camps of dust;
sand-papers trees; breeds lean cattle;
winnows horses and men, until clay beneath the skin
pools the wet harvest in mirrors for *kabouras*.
Half a year, the puddles turn clay-red eyes to winking clouds
from mountains, blue as dreams,
to a roof-edged benediction of abattoir, hangar and cactus.
Holding the built dam, the corral fence and the nurtured
        casuarina
for a dare to plumb the seed of the day's eye,
a rancher stamps out his square, beaten, bare hour of clay.
His thatched house accretes mud walls,
and a hammock swings, where a woman suckles her child.

Gloria Escoffery

I COME FROM THE NIGGER YARD

Until today, in the middle of the tumult,
when the land changes and the world is all convulsed,
when different voices join to say the same
and different hearts beat out in unison,
where on the aching floor of where I live
the shifting earth is twisting into shape,
I take, again, my nigger life, my scorn,
and fling it in the face of those who hate me;
it is me, the nigger boy, turning to manhood,
linking my fingers,
welding my flesh to freedom.

I come from the nigger yard of yesterday,
leaping from the oppressor's hate
and scorn of myself.
I come to the world with scars upon my soul,
wounds upon my body, fury in my hands.
I turn to the histories of men
and the lives of peoples.
I examine the shower of sparks,
the wealth of the dreams.
I am pleased with the glories,
and sad with the sorrows,
rich with the riches,
poor with the loss.

From the nigger yard of yesterday,
I come with my burden;
to the world of tomorrow,
I turn with my strength.

Martin Carter

HOMESTEAD

Seven splendid cedars break the trades
from the thin gables of my house,
seven towers of song when the trades rage
through their full green season foliage.
But weathers veer; the drought returns;
the sun burns emerald to ochre;
and thirsty winds strip the boughs bare, and
then they are tragic stands of sticks,
pitiful in pitiless noons,
and wear dusk's buskin and the moon's.

And north beyond them lie the fields
which one man laboured his life's days,
one man, wearing his bone,
shaped them as monuments in stone,
hammered them with iron will
and a rugged earthy courage,
and going, left me heritage.
Is labour lovely for a man
that drags him daily into earth, and
returns no fragrance of him forth?

The man is dead but I recall
him in my voluntary verse;
his life was unadorned as bread;
he reckoned weathers in his head,
and wore their ages on his face,
and felt their keenness to his bone,
the sting of sun and whip of rain.
He read day's event from dawn,
and saw the quality of morning
through the sunset mask of evening.

In the fervour of my song
I hold him firm upon the fields
in many homely images.
His ghost's as tall as the tall trees;
he tramps these tracks his business made
by daily roundabout in boots
tougher and earthier than roots;
and every furrow of the earth
and every shaken grace of grass
knows him the spirit of the place.

He was a slave's son, peasant born,
paisan, paisano, those common
men about their fields, world over,
of sugar, cotton, corn or clover,
who are unsung but who remain
perpetual as the passing wind,
unkillable as the frail grass, and
who, from their graves within their graves,
nourish the splendour of the earth
and give her substance, give her worth.

Poets and artists turn, again;
construct your cunning tapestries
upon the ages of their acres,
the endless labour of their years;
still, at the centre of their world,
cultivate the first green graces,
courage, strength and kindliness,
love of man and beast and landscape;
still, sow and graft the primal good,
green boughs of innocence to God.

E. M. Roach

THE SONG OF THE BANANA MAN

Touris', white man, wipin' his face,
met me in Golden Grove market place.
He looked at me ol' clothes brown wid stain,
an' soaked right through wid de Portlan' rain.
He cas' his eye, turn' up his nose;
he says, 'You're a beggar man, I suppose?'
He says, 'Boy, get some occupation;
be of some value to your nation.'

I said, 'By God an' dis big right han',
you mus' recognize a banana man.

'Up in de hills, where de streams are cool,
an' mullet an janga swim in de pool,
I have ten acres of mountain side,
an' a dainty-foot donkey dat I ride,
four Gros Michel, an' four Lacatan,
some coconut trees, an' some hills of yam,
an' I pasture on dat very same lan'
five she-goats an' a big black ram;

'dat, by God an' dis big right han',
is de property of a banana man.

'I leave me yard early-mornin' time
an' set me foot to de mountain climb;
I ben' me back to de hot-sun toil,
an' me cutlass rings on de stony soil,
ploughin' an' weedin', diggin' an' plantin',
till Massa Sun drop back o' John Crow mountain,
den home again in cool evenin' time,
perhaps whistlin' dis likkle rhyme:

(SUNG) 'Praise God an' me big right han',
I will live an' die a banana man.

'Banana day is me special day;
I cut me stems an' I'm on me way;
load up de donkey, leave de lan',
head down de hill to banana stan';
when de truck comes roun', I take a ride
all de way down to de harbour side.
Dat is de night, when you, touris' man,
would change you' place wid a banana man.

'Yes, by God an' me big right han',
I will live an' die a banana man.

'De bay is calm, an' de moon is bright;
de hills look black for de sky is light;
down at de docks is an English ship,
restin' after her ocean trip,
while on de pier is a monstrous hustle,
tallymen, carriers, all in a bustle,
wid stems on deir heads in a long black snake,
some singin' de songs dat banana men make:

'like, (SUNG) 'Praise God an' me big right han',
I will live an' die a banana man.

'Den de payment comes, an' we have some fun,
me, Zekiel, Breda an' Duppy Son.
Down at de bar near United Wharf,
we knock back a white rum, bus' a laugh,
fill de empty bag for further toil
wid saltfish, breadfruit, coconut oil,
den head back home to me yard to sleep
a proper sleep dat is long an' deep.

'Yes, by God an' me big right han',
I will live an' die a banana man.

'So when you see dese ol' clothes brown wid stain,
an' soaked right through wid de Portlan' rain,
don't cas' you' eye or turn up you' nose,
don't judge a man by his patchy clothes;
I'm a strong man, a proud man, an' I'm free,
free as dese mountains, free as dis sea;
I know m'self, an' I know me ways,
an' will sing wid pride to de end o' me days:

(SUNG) 'Praise God an' me big right han',
I will live an' die a banana man.'

Evan Jones

ON THE BRIGHT SIDE

Sometimes, I marvel at my perfection.
I am, continually, surprised to find
I have two eyes and two ears, each
in the right place; and when I cut
myself, shaving, my blood clots.
Next day, new flesh will have grown.
I have two arms of equal length (approx.),
each terminating
in four fingers and an apposite thumb,
and their co-ordination is, absolutely, perfect.
Being male, my breasts remain, appropriately,
stunted; but I am, completely, served
by the machineries of joy.
Stomach and duodenum assimilate food,
reject, and process the unusable; and my liver
does whatever it is that livers do.
But, most of all, I wonder at the material,
enclosing me, like a bag, sensual with nerve-endings,
fitting, perfectly, and covering me, all over;
flexible, elastic, it would put any mac to shame:
my waterproof skin.

Arthur Raymond

POEM
(a fragment from 'Charles Mingus, Hurrah!')

Where I'm at! Where you're at!
Where we're all at!
The sustained hurt is a testimony.
The dying Jamaican youth stumbles
to his predictable death
on one glassful of confusion.
Where are *you* at?

Sebastian Clarke

AT THE MOMENT

To be exiled
is to know your own tune
and not to sing it;
the steps of your own dance
and not dance;
remain in darkness
knowing the light.

At the moment,
then,
and only then,
song,
dance,
intoxication of light,
zinc
and lead
turn gold!

Milton Williams

THE INVISIBLE

They don't even know
        that I'm here.

They don't even feel
        that I'm here.

They see me, but they don't see
        me.

I'm here.

                        Rudolph Kizerman

HUSA

I' beatin' me husa drum
all year long, an'
I ain't waitin' for no 'ficial festival;
all I want is me personal bacchanal.

Bin-bibi-din-bong!
Bibi-din-bong!

We beatin' Oil-drum,
 Dus'-bin, Bamboo, Zapa-too, an'
makin' music from any ol' shoe'.

Walkin' from town to St. James,
I' moverin' like I' in Olympic Games,
an 'eatin' me roti
wit' me rum in me han',
while I' lookin' for a husa band
to join.

Brother! I' jumpin' up in the husa band
in me own mind, yes, an'
even makin' 'eadstan', an'
'oldin' plenty woman roun' them waist, an'
feelin' the people' rhythm,
as I' jumpin' up
in the husa band
in me own mind.

108

I ain' waitin' for no 'ficial festival;
all I want is me personal bacchanal.

Bin-bibi-din-bong!
Bibi-din-bong!

I' jumpin' up
in the husa band
in me own mind.

Bin-bibi-din-bong!
Bibi-din-bong!

Frank John

HURRICANE

The window saw.
The door welcomed.
I was expecting no one.
Last year lay sleeping, but
surprise set me free,
stole the keyhole, and
imprisoned the key.

The void, held in custody,
pronounced me absent.
Looking-glass questioned my memory
while squares went on erasing the circles,
and I lay sprawled in the will.

Someone's shadow invited
the 20th Century.
Nineteen hollow centuries, backwards,
strayed along the skyline, and
the world rolled on, tenuous,
a double-edged sword, furious,
like an angry sea, slipping the leash.

Dragged back a captive sea,
it took a bite at the light
from the shipwreck.
Balconies.
Cities.
Bells.

Someone gave me a letter, and
rushed me along, spiralling.
Deserts, rivers, shores and seas ran
away; the sky became my enemy; and
my dream blew away.

Stop me!
Let me be still!
Give me a name:
wind is my surname.

Claude Lushington

3. The Fire of Involvement

HOMECOMING

The wind is making countries,
in the air; clouds dim, golden
as Eldorado voyages.
                    Those hills
harbour a sea of dreams, they told
us; and, as children, we were sad,
wanting a rainbow.
                    Now, heart-sailed
from home, I name them
Orient, Africa,
New York, London's white legend: the
ports have a welcoming ring; no end
to their richness, their tumble.
The sirens sing.
                    But, again,
again, these hot and coffee streets reclaim
my love. Carts rumble.
The long horn of a higgler's voice,
painting the shadows mid-day
brown, cries about harvest:
and the wind calls back
blue air across the town: it tears
the thin topographies of dream, and it blows
me, as by old, familiar maps,
to this affectionate shore, green
and crumpling hills,
like paper in the Admiral's fist.

The rain comes down.
                    There is a kind of tune
we must promise our children,
a shape that the quadrant measures,
no North
to turn them
away from the dissonant cities,
the salt songs,
the hunger of journeys.
                    It is time to plant
feet in our earth. The heart's-metronome
insists on this arc of islands
as home.

Dennis Scott

A KIND OF KARATE

When I, no longer, pretended
we differed
(yet, also, the same
in my skull),
the days became very simple
and disturbing, like metal knives.

They grew tall as my house.
I remember the garden
we played in, as round
as a dream,
my love,
contracted to that space,
                              hedged
by his dangerous envy.
I wanted, forever,
to be quiet with him, guiltless,
determining peace by my own kind
of friendship.

This morning, I wake,
and look;
someone has spread the rough map
of *here*, out: mountains, the tiled
town, quiet, and home:
land under our heels,
and shining, like knives,
the sea about, *dojo*, mat of my country.

I call to him, 'What is
this terrible thing
you require?'
Smiling,
he whispers the ritual
challenge,

                      'I come to you

with my hands
empty.'

Dennis Scott

CUB

Here's an animal,
home-skinned, two-headed,
and with his eyes, shut,
sleeping. He dreams
a little, maybe, preferring
to hunt alone, when
the real hunger doubles him
over, in grief, back
to positions of the one, true
longing we share:
foetus.
                              And game he plays!
(Easier as tournament goes
on) shapes his mood
to our eyes' reflection:
he's what, now, we wish
him to think he's made
of, boy.
                              No kills yet
to his credit, not
weaned from kindness.

Till one noon,
shrugging our love
for a bold new coat,
he'll open his eyes
and his mouth wide as

the Guernica horse
to scream his coming
of age at the trembling house;
the walls will fall down,
and the pack
take him to council as
one (they
recognising some new beast)
that walks the world without
mercy.

But, this one's special
(I've heard that each forked
creature goes singularly
and unduplicated: he with two heads
not least),

one mouth roaring
the terrible hunger of his mind,
the other, still, infinitely kind.

Dennis Scott

THE TIGHTROPE WALKER
(*For* N.W.M.)

Later, they said that
he should have had more

of the acrobat, of the circus
in his saunter, more tinsel
and more trumpet in his dream.
They wanted tumblers, tyrannies,
all the spangled flattery
he would not pretend;
he went too straightly, balancing
his vision towards
our common end.

You measure a man by
the space that his going makes;
the air, now, is full of his absence;
the tent is still.
Gather his books and the medals.
The lights go down
over the quiet arena,
over the sea and the hill;
the music descends
to a funeral sorrow.
Silence each clown.
But, when the show begins again,

and the big drums beat,
and the grinning performers circle the ring
on their deceptive feet,
remember the high road, he walked, higher
than the glitter or the glory
of the show,
following the simpleness
of that determined cord
across the dangerous
tempting fame below.

Dennis Scott

WHO'LL SEE ME DIVE?

Who'll see me dive? Look! here am I
at the crest, arms flung out like a t.v.
antenna, like Jesus,
and not a God soul on the street.

Who'll see me dive? Twelve on a Saturday
night, and not even a taxi;
everybody's gone discotheque
or bram. Lousy night for my leap.

Better look up instead. But all I
can see is the friendly sky,
trafficked by stars whose sheen could con
me out of my long flight down.

Then look sideways, raking the south
for a hint of sea. But that view's dark
as the wish which propelled me up.
Crazed uncertain, my eyes pivot

back into self, confused, close down,
then alight on the street again.
No target yet. Only a cat
like Lowell's skunk, dredging for scraps.

Perhaps, I should put it off;
but how can I with that final note
pencilled against a change-of-heart?
May as well kill it now, this life

poised like a dash so long at death.
Nevertheless, still would have wished
for more *bangarang*: people skirt-
ing the base of Sunley like dirt,

filing my screwed hurt into hate:
some *rass* slung up like a pellet,
spurring the crash, stoning me down
onto *them*. At last, pure weapon!

Tony McNeill

VALLEY PRINCE

Me one, way out in the crowd,
I blow the sounds, the pain,
but not a soul
would come inside my world
or tell me how it' true.
I love a melancholy baby,
sweet, with fire in her belly;
and like a spite
the woman turn' a whore.
Cool and smooth around the beat
she wake' the note inside me
and I blow me mind.

Inside here, me one
in the crowd, again,
and plenty people
want me blow it straight.
But straight is not the way; my world
don' go so; that is lie.
Oonu gimme back me trombone, man:
i's time to blow me mind.

Mervyn Morris

SQUID

The old colonial steamship
is gone now. No towering flanks
distress these wharves, no funnels, flag-like,
straddle the storehouse, only

Black hands shake abandoned crates
and trapped filth
bulges and breaks as, fleeing,
the flushed sun
is dragged beneath horizon.

And yet, the old colonial darkness
seeps into this waterfront tomb
finding the crates unforced.

A dry wind
stammers and falls.

'If I had known,
I would not have come . . .'

Too late, for now
some rage retreats from cheated eyes;
some
flung sperm spirals to the ocean's womb, where,

born
and grown
and gathering now
about its yellowed stare,
a hunchbacked Blackness wells and stirs.

Elsewhere, leashed cars
snarl like teeth in hysterical highways
('The ayes have it! The ayes have it! Pow pow pow pow!')
and the ringed road's hurled, throttling lasso
·pronounces us finally
beasts.

II

Waves,
   unseen,
      heard only,
Thump against the sterile pier
with the dull, unheeded, endless
sorrow of an African drum.

A dirty moon
drifts like a cork in a cesspit of clouds.

In the widening shadows of the humped
shore, eight
tentacles grip a fisherman's oar.

Wayne Brown

SOUL ON ICE

Instantly, the horizon tilts and whirls
to a white sky, emptied of geese.
Listen. It seems

years since the ant-trek team
of huskies scrawled across this snow,
leaving no trail, leaving

me, the landscape, shimmering, waiting for words.
The syntax of solitude is thickening
my tongue. I cannot bend my back.

What noise is that, the river's roar,
or the city's avalanche of words,
crashing and breaking far away?

Shall I be a child? Shall I
die alone, away from the dogs' hot
breath? I can decipher nothing now.

The sun's effort
glows and fades. White napkins
are floating down. Shall I

startle the fossils, while yet I think
of trees, white-thighed, whipping about
for our lost-love, yours too?

This is our pale vaudeville,
so let us dance: the ape's skeleton, erect,
and the ghost. Characters of the

Apocalypse! I am bored
with stares. What I want now
are all those truths the prophets told,

memory, infancy, where it went wrong,
the ice-flash, the
mastodon, the mastodon!

Listen.
It seems years. . . .

Wayne Brown

A DEDICATION TO CUBA

Among the clouds,
the tattered remains of a symbol:
a new generation will come
to rule the land,
and stand in our naked earth.

Like the sea,
and like the tide,
and like the flicker
of an unending candle:
the greatest are there,
the bearded heroes,
the new men,
the earth of the new order.

Standing like rocks, mountains,
and guardians:
the true cause, the living truths,
the overwhelming patronage of time,
the sons of the casual finality.

Every new season
brings its excitement
of buried history,
strange as it seems,
heaped under a dream
of reality.

Faustin Charles

SOUCOUYANT

Witch of flying fire,
creative in her pact with Satan,
complex in her Island's ancestry,
she boils blood in a barrel of molasses,
and melts blue and red candles
with the heat emanating
from her passionate personality.
Vampire, shining like a star,
scowling in the glory of the moon,
panting schemes of demonic orgies,
in her repertoire of smoky concoctions,
she weaves seductive spells
around faithless, labouring men.

An old woman rubs red lavender
on her wrinkled face,
and massages her rheumatic limbs,
contemplating her double identity.
She is known as 'Ma' in the village,
and loved by everybody;
no one suspects the evil in her walk.

Night comes, and she sheds her skin,
snake-like, with the venom
of her tormented age;
then she rises, glowing like a fire-fly;
her fanged compass spins,

and she sways, rising, flying,
encircling the trees,
and finally perching on a window-sill.

Corn the skin with salt:
skin-a-me; skin-a-me!
Throw rice grains in her way:
skin-a-me; skin-a-me!
Count the grains,
quick, quick,
before the light of day!

Faustin Charles

VOICES

Behind a green tree the whole sky is dying,
in a sunset of rain, in an absence of birds.
The large pools of water lie down in the street
like oceans of memory sinking in sand.
The sun has committed itself, far too soon,
in the trial of conquest, where triumph is rain.
O flower of fire, in a wide vase of air,
come back, come back to the house of the world.

Scarlet stone is a jewel of death
to be found in the sand, when the ocean is dry;
and the life of the light will stay somewhere else
near the rain and the tree when these are alone.
O first sprouting leaf, and last falling fruit,
your roots came before you were given to air.

Sky only blossomed because man grew tall
from the edge of the water where stones fell and sank.
And that strange dissolution of shape into spirit
was traced from a snail and was found in a word:
O flower of fire, in a wide vase of air,
come back, come back to the house of the world.

Martin Carter

LOOKING AT YOUR HANDS

No!
I will not still my voice!
I have too much to claim;
if you see me looking at books
or coming to your house
or walking in the sun,
know that I look for fire!

I have learnt
from books, dear friend,
of men dreaming and living
and hungering in a room without a light
who could not die since death was far too poor
who could not sleep to dream,
but dreamed to change the world.

And so, if you see me
looking at your hands,
listening when you speak,
marching in your ranks,
you must know
I do not sleep to dream,
but dream to change the world.

Martin Carter

YOU ARE INVOLVED

This I have learned:
today, a speck;
tomorrow, a hero;
hero or monster,
you are consumed!

Like a jig,
the loom shakes;
like a web,
the pattern is spun;
all are involved,
and all are consumed!

Martin Carter

POEMS OF SHAPE AND MOTION

(I)

I was wondering if I could shape this passion,
just as I wanted, in solid fire.
I was wondering if the strange combustion of my days,
the tension of the world inside me,
and the strength of my heart
were enough.

I was wondering if I could stand as tall,
while the tide of the sea rose and fell;
if the sky would recede, as I went,
or the earth would emerge, as I came
to the door of the morning, locked against the sun.

I was wondering if I could make myself
nothing but fire, pure and incorruptible;
if the wound of the wind on my face
would be healed by the work of my life;
or the growth of the pain in my sleep
would be stopped in the strife of my days.

I was wondering if the agony of the years
could be traced to the seed of the hour;
if the roots that spread out in the swamp
ran too deep for the issuing flower.

I was wondering if I could find myself
all that I am in all I could be;
if all the population of stars
would be less than the things I could utter;
and the challenge of space in my soul
be filled by the shape I become.

(II)

I walk slowly in the wind,
watching myself, in things I did not make,
in jumping shadows, and in limping cripples,
dust on the earth
and houses tight with sickness,
deep, constant pain,
the dream without sleep.

I walk slowly in the wind,
hearing myself in the loneliness of a child,
in a woman's grief, which is not understood;
in coughing dogs, when midnight lingers long
on stones, on streets;
and then on echoing stars
that burn all night,
and suddenly go out.

I walk slowly in the wind,
knowing myself in every moving thing;
in years and days and words
that mean so much;
in strong hands that shake;
long roads that walk;
and in the deeds that do themselves;
and all this world
and all these lives to live.

I walk slowly in the wind,
remembering scorn and naked men in darkness
and huts of iron, rivetted to the earth,
cold huts of iron standing on the earth
like rusting prisons.

Each wall is marked,
and each wide roof is spread
like some dark wing,
casting a shadow
or a living curse.

I walk slowly in the wind,
remembering me in the surging river,
in the drought
and in the merciless flood
and in the growth
and in the life of man.

I walk slowly in the wind,
and the birds are swift,
and the sky is blue like silk.

From the big sweeping ocean of water,
an iron ship, rusted and brown,
anchors itself;
and the long river runs like a snake,
silent and smooth.

I walk slowly in the wind;
I hear my footsteps, echoing down the tide,
echoing like a wave on the sand
or a wing on the wind, echoing,
echoing,
a voice in the soul,
a laugh in the funny silence.

I walk slowly in the wind;
I walk, because I cannot crawl or fly.

Martin Carter

THE INTRUDER

I haven't come to conquer
you with the forces of
the city,
nor to scrape your fields
of lilies
and see them wither
while I stand on the plain.
I've come to pick your berries
and to listen to the contentment
of the Solitaire.
I wish to hug the Eucalyptus
and to tiptoe among
the sleeping willows,
and gaze down
upon the city far below.
Yet I feel like an intruder,
Blue Mountain,
a flea scampering up
your dusty spine!

Basil Smith

SPEAKING TWICE

You know, if I were to tell you that I love you,
I'm sure you'd say, 'Why do you pick on me?'
And I, with my old man's ways, would writhe
in sheets of smiles of embarrassment,
and force a private *double entendre*.

Yet, how plain it is! You do not want
my love, at all. But aren't you being,
reluctantly, a little too polite? For you hurt
me, all the same. Then, of course, the beauty
of innocent truth is its licking

the wound it inflicts. Even so, I should persist
in blowing rings of purposed
ambiguity. Why wouldn't you
say, simply, 'Go to hell!' An old man doesn't lie
to himself: he finds soothing explanations
and comfort in his spinning-wheel.

Emmanuel Jean-Baptiste

POEM

It takes a mighty fire
to create a great people.

It takes a mighty fire
to smelt true steel;
to create and temper steel
needs patience and endurance.

The mould is not yet made, perhaps,
that can unite and make the people one.
But more important than the mould
is the temper of the steel,
the spirit of the people.

And when that steel is smelted
and when that steel is tempered
and when that steel is cast
what a people that people will be!

H. D. Carberry

NO JOKE

No more damn' nonsense;
no more damn' hypocrisy;
no more 'We shall overcome!'

No more darkness;
no more light;
just life!

The black man's fighting
for the right to be himself.

No more sitting
on his backside, again!

He has no intention
of taking any more inflicted pain.

Black people with *soul*
are free to destroy their slavery
and join hands in unity.

Dance the calypso, jazz, blues;
dance it without shoes.
Rock-steady without fear;
man, beware;
rock-steady without care;
the people break away.

We ain't making fun;
we'll fight in the snow
or in the sun.

Frank John

VARIATION

Whose world was shell was his, which stood
on poles, too slim for human thought,
devised of such material as quivers at the touch
of bated breath and cannot stand the pressure of a hair.
Too much, too little, in the casting mould,
inconsiderate of time, too slow in movement of dream,
he defied your signals like a daylight bat,
charting a crazy course in an empty world.
He awoke, too late, in a blinding light, and softly turned away
to count his winnings and his wounds.

Now he knows what this green season has unsprung
in the earth, waiting for a sudden leap to light
and annihilation, and his world unspins
like the spring of a clock gone mad with winding.

Samuel Selvon

ONE FLOWER

While men watched the cities disintegrating,
princesses saw me building our community of new people
who, once, were write-offs in the old world.
We toiled with a vigour that made them ask,
'For what?' and 'Where are you going?' even 'Why?'
It was late in the year, and their peace feelers were out,
but we could not hear; our hands were full.
The only sounds were the hammers and saws
of the carpenters. Music we call it.
Bombs fell around us.

Those, they could gather, were thrown into their jails.
We went on. They could not tear down our town.
Their bombs kept raining but our building stood;
it shone like a light among the ruins.
They could not understand; our foundation was solid.
It is made of the new material: IDEA.

Michael Abdul Malik

A POUND OF FLESH AT MARKET PRICE

I want to shape you on the anvil of my will,
the blacksmith says to metal. To hell with
pride, the nail replies, burying itself in flesh.

I want to sharpen you fine on the grindstone
of my mind, the mechanic says to tools. To the devil
with lusts, the cutlass replies, driving itself
into bitter sugar cane; I do not want blood,
just sweetness of sweat for my teacups.

Good-bye, the ironmonger says, selling nails, axes
and cutlasses to the poor; I want to part with you
for sweet potatoes; I do not need the comfort
of dungarees, though; for I live well in your name
if able to forget the deeper secrets
of my fears and the abyss of my hopes.

We give ourselves to you, so that
we remain forgiven, the cutlery's retort to the ironmonger's
    gibe;
we also dream of an affectionate bride to lie with,
a pleasure house cunningly made, and strange diamonds,
cut from dust in a wasteland,
where there are no promenades.

Claude Lushington

147

ELEVENTH HOUR

Give me tickets for innocence;
fill my pockets with experience:
I want to sit in tramcars
and clean my windows
with your streetlamps.

I want to test your floorboards,
where the echoes remain still,
hidden in the shadow
of her footprints.

She, too, has been in the traffic accident,
in the factory that falls out of the chimney,
in the ships and trains running late, due to
the schedule, upended, when patching
the network or wagon, clinging
to my feet. I cannot plant
my footprints in the blob
of sealing wax, sticking to my ceiling.

But the dustman, at last, wants cash,
before he starts
to collect the ash.

Claude Lushington

4. The Blaze of the Struggle

SQUATTER'S RITES

Peas, corn, potatoes; he had
planted himself,
king of a drowsy hill; no one
cared
how he came to
such green dignity,
scratching his majesty,
among the placid chickens.

But, after a time, after
his deposition, the uncivil wind
snarled anarchy through that
small kingdom. Trees, wild birds
troubled the window,
as though to replace the fowl
that wandered and died of summer;
spiders locked the door,
threading the shuddered moths,
and stabbed their twilight needles through
that grey republic. The parliament of dreams
dissolved. The shadows tilted,
where leaf-white, senatorial lizards
inhabited his chair.

Though one of his sons made it,
blowing *reggae* (he
dug city life),
enough to bury the old Ras,
with respect,
ability, and finally,
a hole in his heart;
and, at night, when the band played
soul, the trumpet
pulse beat
down the hill
to the last post,
abandoned,
leaning in its hole
like a sceptre
among the peas, corn, potatoes.

Dennis Scott

UNCLE TIME

Uncle Time is a' ol', ol' man.
All year long, 'im wash' 'im foot, in de sea,
long, lazy years, on de wet san',
an' shake' de coconut tree dem,
quiet–like, wid 'im sea–win' laughter,
scrapin' 'way de lan'.

Uncle Time is a spider–man, cunnin' an' cool.
'Im tell' y'u, 'Watch de 'ill an' y'u see me.'

Huhn!
F'you' eye no' quick enough f'see
'ow 'im move', like mongoose.
Man, y'u t'ink 'im fool'?

F'me Uncle Time smile', black as sorrow.
'Im voice is sof' as bamboo leaf;
but, Lawd, me Uncle' cruel.

When 'im play' in de street
wid you' woman, watch 'im! By tomorrow,
she' dry as cane–fire, bitter as cassava;
an' when 'im teach' you' son, long after
y'u walk wid stranger, an' you' bread is grief.
Watch 'ow 'im spin' web roun' you' 'ouse, an' creep'
inside; an', when 'im touch' y'u, weep!

Dennis Scott

153

ODE TO BROTHER JOE

Nothing can soak
Brother Joe's tough sermon,
his head swollen
with certainties.

When he lights up a *s'liff*,
you can't stop him,
and the door to God, usually shut,
gives in a rainbow gust.

Then, it's time for the pipe,
which is filled with its water base
and handed to him for his blessing.
He bends over the stem,
goes into the long grace,
and the drums start;

the drums start:
Haile Selassie I,
Jah Rastafari!
And the room fills with the power
and beauty of blackness,
a furnace of optimism.

But the law thinks different.
This evening, the *Babylon* catch
Brother Joe, in his act of praise,
and carry him off to the workhouse.

Who'll save Brother Joe? Haile
Selassie is far away
and couldn't care less,
and the promised ship

is a million light years
from Freeport.
But the drums, in the tenement house,
are sadder than usual, tonight,

and the brothers suck hard
at their *s'liffs* and pipes:
before the night's over,
Brother Joe has become a martyr,

but still in jail.
And only his woman,
who appreciates his humanity more,
will deny herself of the weed, tonight,
to hire a lawyer
and put up a real fight.

Meantime, in the musty cell,
Joe invokes, almost from habit,
the magic words:
Haile Selassie I,
Jah Rastafari!
But the door is real,
and remains shut.

                                   Tony McNeill

I am wired for sound. I live
in a ringing network of bones
more alarming than skeletons.
Even asleep, I buzz and hive.

Constantly bee-high, I alight
on external flowers, pushing
through petals with my pink snake-tongue
in search of an exit, or light.

But neither lives here; nor silence.
The hum of internal traffic
crazes within this place; soon hooks
me back out, both flaccid and tense.

Returned to my sounding abyss,
I stand outside flowers and bees,
who, responding to easy cues
deftly, relax in the darkness.

Tomorrow will re-start their lives
with sunlight's certain ignition.
I sleep with my eyes wide open,
uneasy among my shrill hives.

When something snaps, as it could do,
I'll be carried off to a place
sound-proof and new. If not, I'll stay
here and marry. Or split in two.

Tony McNeill

SAINT RAS

Every stance seemed crooked. He had
not learned to fall in with the straight
queued, capitalistic, for work.
He was uneasy in traffic.

One step from that intersection
could, maybe, start peace. But he dread-
fully missed; could never proceed
with the rest, when the white signal

spelled safe journey. Bruised, elbowed-in,
his spirit stopped at each crossing,
seeking the lights for the one sign
indicated to take him across

to the true island of Ras.
But outside, his city of dreams
was no right-of-passage it seemed.
Still-anchored by faith, he idled

inside his hurt harbour & even
his innocent queen posed red
before his poised, inchoate bed.
Now exiled more, or less,

he retracts his turgid divinity;
returns to harsh temporal streets
whose uncertain crossings reflect
his true country. Both doubt and light.

Tony McNeill

MARINERS

who are
the night-cruisers
slicing through dark
dim on the foredeck
scanning for shark

we are
the *sea-fearers*
sick in the deep
bilious in daylight
troubled asleep

we are
the sea-searchers
scaling the night
keen in the darkness
fish-eyed in light

Mervyn Morris

DEVILFISH

Fat butterfly, fleshed in sin,
fat Nazi.
Daily, they climb

away from it, these wide-eyed fish,
break surface in octaves of scattershot, guns.
They'd choose a green nightmare any day by far

to its thick, whitening
absence. Ice-white, whiter
than thighs, than milk, men

in retreat utterly exhaust themselves.
In the end,
caps in hand, falling in,

we enter its gaze, the gloom-cell.
Spent, anxious Christians,
we're taken in;

we endlessly extend
its dreams.
Now

stuffed up like God, the state,
on us, the sea's
lumpen-proletariat,

it gathers its nightmare in
and hurls it-
self into our shattering air.

Marching in pairs, no one sees
the wintering stream of it erupt,
nor hears the thunder of its

recoil:
and the fisherman, riding a storybook calm,
whistles for luck as he sends his lure down.

Wayne Brown

DEATH OF A COMRADE

Death must not find us thinking that we die.

Too soon, too soon,
our banner was draped for you.

I would prefer
the banner in the wind,
not bound so tightly,
in a scarlet fold,
not sodden,
with your people's tears,
but flashing on the pole
we bare,
down and beyond
this dark lane of rags.

Dear Comrade,
if it must be
that you speak no more with me,
nor smile no more with me,
nor march no more with me,
then, let me be patient and calm;
for even now the greener leaf explodes;
the sun brightens the stone;
and all the rivers burn.

Now, from the mourning vanguard,
moving on,
dear Comrade,
I salute you,
and I say
death will not find us thinking that we die.

Martin Carter

CARTMAN OF DAYCLEAN

Now, to begin the road:
broken land, ripped like a piece of cloth;
iron cartwheel, rumbling in the night;
hidden man, consistent in the dark;
sea of dayclean, washing on the shore;
heart of an orphan, seeking orphanage.

Now, to begin the road:
the bleeding music of apellant man
starts like a song but fades into a groan;
the supra-star will burn as blue as death
and his hopes are whitened,
starched with grief and pain;
yet, questing man is a heavy, laden cart
whose iron wheels will rumble in the night,
whose iron wheels will spark against the stone
and granite burden of the universe.

Now, to begin the road:
hidden cartman, fumbling for a star,
across the brooding city,
like a mound of coal,
to journey's end,
the prostrate coughing hour,
with sudden welcome,
will take him to his dream;
with sudden farewell,
will send him to his grave.

Martin Carter

165

I CLENCH MY FIST

You come, in warships, terrible with death.
I know your hands are red with Korean blood.
I know your finger trembles on a trigger.
And yet, I curse you, stranger, khaki clad.
    British soldier, man, in khaki,
    careful how you walk.
    My dead ancestor, Accabreh,
    is groaning in his grave;
    at night, he wakes and watches,
    with fire in his eyes,
    because you march upon his body
    and stamp upon his heart.
Although you come, in thousands, from the sea,
although you walk, like locusts, in the street,
although you point your gun, straight at my heart,
I clench my fist above my head;
I sing my song of freedom!

Martin Carter

ON THE FOURTH NIGHT OF HUNGER STRIKE

I have not eaten for four days.
My legs are paining; my blood runs slowly.
It is cold, tonight; the rain is silent and sudden,
and, yet, there is something warm inside me.

At my side, my comrade lies in his bed,
watching the dark;
a cold wind presses, chilly, on the world.
It is the night of a Christmas day,
a night in December;
we watch each other,
noting how time passes.

Today, my wife brought me a letter from a comrade;
I hid it in my shirt from the soldiers.
They could not know my heart was reading 'Courage';
they could not dream my skin was touching 'Struggle'.

But, Comrade, now, I can hardly write, at all;
my legs are paining; my eyes are getting dark.
It is the fourth night of a hunger strike,
a night in December.
I hold your letter, tightly, in my hand.

Martin Carter

POEM
(a fragment from 'What is it?')

What is it? I wonder.
What is it?

Is it a curse on the earth,
inside the flesh,
within the tissues,
deep in the blood,
black in the bone?

Is it in the hurricane,
in the head,
in the marrow,
in the heart,
in the soul?

What is it?

I feel the world around me,
like an acid rind.
I see the hate
and the frustration,
lodged in the head,
in the heart,
in the soul.

And, when I turn,
I face the jungle inside.

Frank John

POEM

*(a fragment from 'The New Ships',
taken from* Masks)

Could these soft huts
have held me?
Wattle daubed on wall
straw-hatted roofs,

seen my round or-
dering, when kicked to life
I cried
to the harsh light around me?

If you should see someone
coming this way
send help, send help, send help
for I am up to my eyes in fear.

And beware
cried Akyere
do not trust strangers.
In their watery eyes
I see dangers.
Hooks jerk
in their smiles,
lurking capture;
sticks

from their stares
are a dry beach
of sand's pain,

bleaching bones
of despair,
your life's
fear.

Do not trust
strangers.
Smell the danger:
cassava cooked
skin that the
wind brings;
their sin
stretches like
smoke, dis-
appears in the white
wind, but re-
mains, re-
mains to stain
our truth with its
stench; and when
night comes,
when night
comes, chok-
ing my eyes'
throat, the fire
is drenched
in fright's
phantoms:
sasabonsam
of darkness
where even the deep-
est drum trembles.

So beware
cried Akyere
beware
the clear
eyes, the near
ships, the
cast lines,
sweet cargoes
of promises.
Beware the steer'd
smiles, their
teeth's rock,
the white
fathoms.

Edward Brathwaite

FOR DENIS WHO WAS A DRUM

What can we do
but hold
hope
in this agony,

in this waiting silence,
this tight beginning,
this restructuring
of new pain
for another generation
of birth,
of dying;

what
but love?

And
to love *is* a violence;
love is a violent understanding.

You heard
the drum,
searching,
inside
your void
and inside
your birthright of terror;

and you named the names
of love, involvement
and commitment
from the chaos.

You shaped love
with both hands,
black and white,
a violent love of understanding.

Yours was an agony
of a torn spirit,
restructuring,
searching,
and always the quick, shy laughter,
the gaiety of being,
the explosion of angered loving.

You chose;
you chose;
you chose
the drum-sound:
love is to be a drum,
and love is also a violent dying.

With a mouth,
uncertain
uncertain
in its beginnings,
in its trembling certainty,
a mouth that stamped you, man,
in this three-fingered world;
a mouth that stamped you, black,
in the divisions,
in the shattered concepts
of your accident of birth;

you chose love
and hope
from the grey schizoid murder.

Walk good,
in peace,
in love,
in the drum track of hope.

Marina Maxwell

THIS LAND

Sun, sea, shady mango groves, and
canefields that look like golf courses
from the air, and
deep, dark, turbulent rivers
are the mainstreams of my land.
The land lives better
than the people who own it,
nurture it,
care
and caress it,
day by day,
from generation
to generation.
We are outlived
by our livlihood,
through no fault of it's own.
We planted hope,
and reaped havoc.
We dreamed dreams,
and awoke with
disillusionment,
swimming in our eyes.
Gods
have fallen,
and died,
run away,
and deserted

their faithful.
A pestilence
is running
rife among us,
devouring our
daughters, and
emasculating
our sons.
The endless
white corridors
of appeal and
salvation
echo,
now, with
hollow laughter.
Severed
heads roll
like falling
coconuts
before many
a black man's
rampaging
imagination.
Great nightmares grow
from broken dreams.
The flag
of retribution
flutters its grizzly
colours in the
howling winds.
Falling rain
settles to reflect
soft, clear visions
that run,
laughing from
our grasp,

with the soft
gait of a million endless
ripples.
When the
canefields
have been razed,
and the mangoes
consumed by
worms soft as pus;
when the rivers
lie dead,
in their dusty graves;
who will be the
last man standing?

Basil Smith

SUICIDE?

Seaweeds
sulk upon the rock.
Black sand teems
with stones.

Here,
in this green
and black holiday place,
death is a white fowl, strangled,
slapping the eye.

Memory searches
the sea of the mind
until, at last, a barb of guilt
harpoons these hours
to his face.

For when his heart,
driven before a gale
of loneliness,
sought in our hearts
a harbour and a home,
no sign we gave
to anchor our compassion
in his soul.

Not silence itself was our sin;
for touching hands
turn silence to a delicate,
exquisite thing, slender
breath of a dawn campfire
on this beach, and eloquent
as a lone seagull's flight.

Why is tenderness usually late
or, if it does come,
frail as foam?

Judy Miles

PRAY FOR RAIN

In seasons of drought
the dry land cracks;
leaves turn from green
to pale yellow.

On the streets
the asphalt reflects
the furious energy
of its crystalled burden.

'It's seasonal,' the people say.
'Pray for rain.'

Drought is not only the way
Nature affects men and crops;
it is the living lie
of all of us: young men,
green-vitalled
in industry,
withering to an absurd anonymity.

Comrades,
perpetual drought is not our heritage!

Like garbage on the downheap,
we're piled high,
forced to exhaust ourselves,
and be divested of all our power.

Crack!
Decay!
And burn!

Comrades,
perpetual drought is not our heritage!

Milton Williams

CHE

In this dark-grained news-photograph, whose glare
is rigidly composed as Caravaggio's,
the corpse glows candle-white on its cold altar,

its stone Bolivian Indian butcher's slab,
and stares till its waxen flesh begins to harden
to marble, to veined, Andean iron;
from your own fear, *cabron*, its pallor grows;

it stumbled from your doubt, and for your pardon
burnt in brown trash, far from the embalming snows.

Derek Walcott

NEGATIVES

A newsclip: the invasion of Biafra:
black corpses wrapped in sunlight
sprawled on the white glare, entering, what's its name,
the central city?

            Someone who's white
illuminates the news behind the news;
his eyes flash with, perhaps, pity:
'The Ibos, you see, are like the Jews;
very much the situation in Hitler's Germany;
I mean the Hausas' resentment.' I try to see.

I never knew you Christopher Okigbo;
I saw you when an actor screamed 'The tribes!
the tribes!' I catch
the guttering, flare-lit
faces of Ibos,
stuttering, bug-eyed
prisoners of some drumhead tribunal.

The soldiers' helmeted shadows
could have been white, and yours
one of those sun-wrapped bodies on the white road,
entering . . . the tribes! the tribes! their shame . . .
that central city, Christ, what is its name?

Derek Walcott

183

A REVOLUTIONARY CORE: CHE GUEVARA

One spark
lights the twig;
and the pile of wood blazes;
the sky blazes;
one man
lifts his head;
four eyes see blood;
and, in a million brains,
flames of anger light
the funeral-pyre of fear.

Do not worry,
out of season,
if you are the only one
in the village
with clear eyes
or reason;
the enemy is your helper.

So,
stand strong,
and trust your people,
your poor people;
they will not let you down.

Strike hard,
Brother!

Arthur Raymond

SUGAR CANE

The succulent flower bleeds molasses,
as its slender, sweet stalks bend,
beheaded in the breeze.

The green fields convulse golden sugar,
tossing the rain aside,
out-growing the sun,
and carving faces
in the sun-sliced panorama.

The reapers come at noon,
riding the cutlass-whip;
their saliva sweetens everything
in the boiling season.

Each stem is a flashing arrow,
swift in the harvest.

Cane is sweet sweat slain;
cane is labour, unrecognised, lost
and unrecovered;
sugar is the sweet swollen pain of the years;
sugar is slavery's immovable stain;
cane is water lying down,
and water standing up.

Cane is a slaver;
cane is bitter,
very bitter,
in the sweet blood of life.

Faustin Charles

HAUNTED CAUDILLO

Sancho, any Sancho,
a bearded, unpopular soldier,
like a deceitful beggar,
spied the sun-baked skeletons
of the butchered cattle,
bent forward, aloof,
and, then, understood the old cow's ghost,
a re-incarnation,
and a coming battle with poverty,
in the lives of the humble people.

He began, in mourning, shouting
in hurried overtones, swaying
against a daggered heart, an actor,
a *politico* of faithless improvisation, staggering
with guilt
through the ravaged tenements of mockery and disorder,
yet, at times, forcing a smile for the brooding people;
he looked suddenly older,
in his little act of pity,
sombre and disgusted, like a worn-out clown
in a morbid, purple gown.

With an abstract grin,
the new fashion,
his lip hanging, a torn piece of skin, he was there,
as if his 'pain' could be regarded
as a benefit;
indeed, his compatriots had murdered the poor old beast,
making a feast with the flesh
against the sky of *conquistadores*.

The barbarous destroyers, their names: Machado,
Trujillo, Batista,
and Duvalier.
Imagine the impertinence of these puppets,
taking life with such pleasure!

Our Islands, and theirs
lament,
and curse their foundations.

Faustin Charles

TEN YEARS: 1959–1969

I speak, today,
from the heartland, where fires burn
under black lava skin,
threatening volcano,
when my peoples' wrath is full;
there are those three worlds
and mine's the Third,
the Human World.

Spartacus spoke for me,
with gladiators bounding out of cages,
bellowing freedom,
until
slaves tore at the roots of Rome, and
bare hands and bare feet burst
phalanxes asunder.

Spartacus pounded a path
to the wine-dark sea,
but no ships came;
traders, counting profit and loss,
abandoned him to crucifixion
on the Appian Way.

Blood, buried at the foot of his cross,
exploded out of the pods of time,
scattering seeds like shrapnel;
one fragment, tracing arabesques,

traversed milleniums
to prick Toussaint's heart:
a drop of blood, a flame.
Flowers sprout;
Toussaint shouts,
under a mahoe tree,
holding a rifle high,
'This is your liberty!'

Toussaint died, betrayed,
in the fortress of Joux,
in the cold fortress of Joux.
Christophe and Dessalines were deaf,
but Bolivar heard him;
at Boyaca, he burnt his boats,
a pyre,
five defeats, a spiral in smoke,
mangrove and stars
and giddy garlands of foam,
an altar,
rain-frogs, crying to the moon,
crickets, clicking legs like castanets,
and the wind, winnowing its way
through torn shirts, cooling sweat,
sunrise, burgeoning out a new age.

Bolivar spits
a clinker of Dragons' Teeth
and warriors spring up to free a continent;
Bolivar died betrayed,
and under his feet,
little men crept,
stealthy as serpents,
bailiffs, dispossessing him of dreams;
but Nat Turner heard him say,
'It's easier to plough the sea
than to rob us of our liberty for long.'

Nat Turner left a legacy
for John Brown, Copeland, Kagi,
and Emperor Green;
the arsenal, at Harper's Ferry,
exploded with their dreams.

Marx, Engels, Lenin,
three, who breached the ramparts,
finally led a thousand million working men
down paths of thunder;
even the deaf heard them coming.
Martí, awakening, left a testament for Fidel;
the grass was green,
and green the hills of the Sierra Maestra:
Cuba is free!

Ten years, and
echoes of singing drums
tell of Garvey and Fidel,
Malcolm and Fidel,
Lumumba and Fidel:
ten years.
Come back, Africa!
Free!

The jade archipelago,
green islands,
green mainlands,
Caribbean Sea,
Maracaibo to Patagonia must be
a free continent;
Asia, Egypt to the Yellow Sea,
Japan,
the crippled lands,
cry freedom, where
it's harsh to them,

our enemies;
it all speaks softly to me;
it leaves them naked
but it clothed me, and
makes me stand up straight,
while it hobbles them.
Cuba is free!
Ten years!

The grass is innocent
of vampire dreams, money,
slippery with blood,
stock marketeers,
presidents,
ministers, diplomats, delegates,
greedy for the sun's sweat,
gold; the grass is innocent
of chocolate-coated lies,
advertised,
fifty times a day,
at peak viewing time:
the message slipped between images
of cowboys slaughtering Indians,
Blacks rioting,
police
and dollar-grins wide
as streets,
in chrome.

Revolution is a river;
Lenin cracked it, like a whip,
to sweep the stables clean,
from the Baltic to the Yellow Sea.
Fidel, Camilo
and Che
made their own lariat of it
in Cuba.

Then Tet,
the season of the New Year, came
to Saigon, Hue,
to two hundred cities, hamlets, towns;
Tet is a season of awakening;
Tet is in my blood, today;
Tet is when we greet the New Year,
every day,
with garlands and guns;
Tet is when maidens,
shedding *leis*,
ware a necklace of grenades.

Brothers of the New Year, everywhere,
carry storms
in famished hearts, following
Spartacus, Toussaint, Bolivar,
Marx, Engels, Lenin,
Martí, Fidel, Camilo
and Che.

Do you remember Cuba,
and the seasons of pain,
when black men were denied
the beaches and the sea's foam?
Men and women
walk tall
in the streets
of Cuba, today.
Cuba is free.
Ten years!
For ever!

Jan Carew

SIMON: HOW MANY BOLIVARS?

Simon: How many Bolivars?
Latest of the brood, Che Guevara.
Salute Jaurez, Zapata again:
horsemen of the Apocalypse,
Andean scorpions of stone,
volcanoes in their hands,
fingers rooted in time,
splitting mirrors and
assaulting fortresses
with their puma paws.

Patriarchs bearing
granite lamps ride
their horses in the moon,
their light like Orion's,
a source of consolation,
bride to the altar of leaves
in a cathedral of timber.
Were they not also a fragment once?

Their poor hands are familar,
their old hearts, unremembered,
by hearts of a thousand years
of recondite truth.

Come to birth, now,
in the midst of clay
and flint; light up
forests,
deserts,
cities,
where congregate
sleeping jaguars,
boa constrictors,
birds like condors.

Heirs to greenheart,
pastured in woodlands,
fire the torch-trumpet again;
rock the ship-eagle once more,
crying with your blood
in a silence of hope, a
magnet clinging to struggle and
bequeathing love, until
earth gives up time and
night collapses at the
new day's red knees.

Claude Lushington

5. *Breaklight*

BREAKLIGHT

Breaklight,
glow!
The old, dark night
was our vision.
We stared the sun
into blindness,
and counted ourselves wise.

Our history,
overcast on the page,
has gained a new impetus.
We've seen through
the writing on the wall.

Let us speak
in our own way!

We sold our souls
for a £
to buy our pay packets
and our positions
on the Cabinet.
We drummed,
hummed,
at the loaves of proposition
and were flattered by adverbial phrases.

When we were young,
we plodded hard.
We were whipped by our alien,
well-placed countrymen.

We were stripped.
We back-pedalled furiously.
We were packed,
like feathered hats,
then sacked, because we called for better wages.

We were the bolt,
the incredible, willing jackpot,
gunned down through the years.
We were the black question-box.
We were slotted into all the avoidable wars,
in foreign places.

We were mules,
fooled,
trained in odd, modish centres.
We were the objects of *mauvaise langue*,
in varying stages,
and we sat on shifting stools,
when we returned.

Breaklight!
We understand might.
We know the power of hate.
We've closed the gaps in our story
for our own good.

Knolly S. La Fortune

FISHERMAN

The scales, like metal, flint his feet;
their empty eyes, like me.
How quicksilver their colours in the heat!
Cool as the oily sea.

With gentle hands, he slits the heart;
and the flesh, as white as milk,
and the ribboned entrails fall apart,
like the fall of coiling silk.

Some day, I, too, shall fish, and find,
on stranger shores than these,
the ribs and muscles of my blind
self, rainbowed from the seas.

Dennis Scott

VISIONARY

One great wing marks his shoulder;
that's why he stumbles
headlong against the sun;
the stuttering wind
bears him
unevenly
across air; wounded
and wilful, he
beats to home,
one arm, shielding
his eyes from
the sun's gold flower,
the hills, folding back
under his journey, the stubborn,
heavy pounding of that
one wing wonderful. Not quite
can earth recall him,
Icarus, this brave
limping bird, making
such fierce way
to a hoped-for home, wise
and wandering with the sun
grown in his eyes.

Dennis Scott

CORTEGE

Their grief's-wind blows him,
three and a half miles, home
to freedom, their black hands,
limp, lowered, like flags,
feet, stuttering
an alphabet of faith;

for his armour is,
finally, bronze; his weapon,
silence, and that green farm wagon
thousands attend, his chariot.

                    This last
march is the loneliest.

                    Yet,
concealed, in the slow mules'-
clatter, the mourners'-
feet,
measuring loss
by the long Atlantic street,

                         he shares
a dream that hope,

in this funeral harvest of lilies,
will let freedom ring,
the wounding, sworded South
healed in some ploughshare Spring.

Dennis Scott

RESURRECTIONS

There's nothing delicate

about this tree they chopped.
The blunted bole
has healed a makeshift grey. Each day,
the rain applies its poultices
of dust. Patient, it seems;
it seems;

                    and nothing tender in her mouth.
Her mouth has eaten the leavened bread
of yes, ma'am, no ma'am, in a place of salt.
One of her men died
in a war, three more at birth,
one, from a tree, fell down;
so, she fell down, again,
each Sunday, at the mercy seat,
sang hymns of healing,
as she swept the floor. Waiting for rain.

And, one day, soon, she won't be
out to work. Sick.
She's been 'bred'; the gardener
chopped her into life, they say.
No wasted glory,

but with sudden flesh,
the tree empties its longing to the light,
invincible, and green.

Dennis Scott

THE CRACK

Today, I thought I glimpsed death
in the bougainvillaeas;
it had no face;
was oblique, as love.
It's what I have been,
and would like to be:
a pure chord, a pure stroke
of pain on a canvas,
something without a face:
all poem.

Tony McNeill

THE OTHER SIDE OF THE MUMMIES

The bee-like hum, in the ears
of the dissociative men, was
the mind's hum. Body lived on
for the keys, in the pores,
that played out the storm.

Body feasted and drew.
A valve in the heart pumped
juice that trickled the harp-
strings taut.
Every will of the wind
made the mind-box hum.

One that I knew
had sloughed his body,
somewhere, or sold it
at auction,
though the shell kept on
to act like a mind through
the pores.

Sound all around them, sense
thicker than fern in the sweat-holes,
these remarkable men drew mind over skin,
threw the key out, and sealed themselves in.

Tony McNeill

SPRING POEM: BROWN'S TOWN
(For Edward Brathwaite)

I

The air shone like glass
all day.
I moved through memories
into the sea,
recalling Long Island springs,
my white love flowering.

II

Mirrors! Transparencies!
Yeats's Ireland,
Robert Lowell's New England,
Rimbaud's castles
rising above my reefs
like thieves.

III

Without the goggles
of borrowed sight,
I cannot make out
my own face.

IV

But the day sparkled;
the day sparkled
like sun striking
a diamond, a prism,

and I moved offshore
into the great
illusive fish-bowl
where captive poets
struggle to school
out of British rule,
to shoal from the craze
of sweet English.

V

Today, I praise
one who half-made it out
to the reef, daring the
sharks with a lonely *reggae*.

Tony McNeill

THE CHILDREN
(*For Edward Brathwaite*)

One swings up–
ward toward the sky,
ascending cool stairs of rope
which end, like magic,
in clouds.

Another does
cartwheels, hurdling grass
into grace.
A third peels cane with the teeth.
The rest, imagination programmed by t.v.,

play cowboy.
Tonight, circled by snow
in a foreign country,
I praise one of the children
who stood alone,

hearing old drums
under the *bam–bam bangarang*,
who passed into man-
hood through the eye of the sun,
and smelted

lonely calypsoes & *soul*
against the long morning of English rule.

Tony McNeill

POEM
(a fragment from 'Rights of Passage')

                    scorched
            hurts continue
            to glow,
            but, my people,
            know
            that the hot
            day will be over
            soon;
            that the star
            that dies, and
            the flamboyant car-
            cass that rots in the road,
            in the gutter,
            will rise,
            rise,
            rise,
            in the butter-
            flies of a new
            and another
            morning;
            that whip rope
            lash, brave
            boast
            and shout
            will dry,
            dry,

dry,
like the bare
bones: powder-
ing spirit-
less stones
of this cold
and alien morning;

for you
old negro Noah
knew
the drip
of rain
and the bird's
call after
the storm;

you heard
the key
turn in the
lock, the

door fly
open onto
the flood-
less green.

Sailed high
your hopes,
then: the
dove returned
from blue
fields with a
green twig,
and the stripped
trees, happy

feathers, could venture
forth. So
Noah,

stepping
softly on the brown
loam, returns
to the firm

earth,
his home. Sharp thorn
against toe,
hard rock

under heel,
feet stretched
into stride,
made you a man

again, and you
followed where the bird called:
remembering woods,

when it was
yesterday:
young, gay,
unblighted

by the mildew
of the world;
woods, where
clear water
clinked. . . .

                    Edward Brathwaite

POEM
(*a fragment from 'Rights of Passage'*)

For tomorrow, the woods
would be fire's delight,
embers alight,
the black

blazing:
purging
the faithless
the flesh into ashes;

no dove
to return with its love
in the morning; no lover
to call like a bird in the green.

Rain drips
from the trees
in the dawn;
in the morn-
ing, bird
calls; green
opens a crack.
Should you

shatter the door
and walk
in the morning
fully aware

of the future
to come?
There is no
turning back.

Edward Brathwaite

THE SURVEY

(*a poem from 'Guyana', taken from* The Gulf)

The surveyor straightens from his theodolite.
'Spirit level,' he scrawls, and instantly
the ciphers, staggering down their columns,
are soldier ants, their panic radiating in the shadow
of a new god, arriving over Aztec anthills.

The sun has sucked his brain pith-dry.
His vision whirls with dervishes; he is dust.
Like an archaic photographer, hooded in shade,
he crouches, screwing a continent to his eye.

The vault that balances on a grass blade, and
the nerve-cracked ground, too close for the word 'measureless',
for the lost concept 'man',
revolve, too slowly, for the fob-watch of his world,
for the tidal markings of the five-year plan.

Ant-sized to God, god to an ant's eyes,
shouldering science, he begins to tread
himself; a world he must triangulate, within three days.

The frothing shallows of the river;
the forest, so distant, that it tires of blue;
the merciless idiocy of green, green . . .

a shape dilates towards him through the haze.

Derek Walcott

NOAH

Everywhere fish wheeled and fled
or died in scores, floating like eggs.
From his mind's ark, Noah,
sailor for the kingdom of Truth's sake,
watched the water close like mouths
over the last known hills. Next day,
he slept, dreaming of haystacks.

Water woke him. He stood, arms folded,
looking from a porthole, thinking nothing,
numbed to a stare by horizon's drone
and the dry patter of rain. On the third day,
decisive, sudden, he dragged
down the canvas curtain and turned
inward to tend his animals, his
animals, waking with novelty.

Locked, driven by fatigue, the ark
beat and beat across the same sea,
bloated, adrift, finding
nothing to fasten to.
Barnacles grew up the sides like sores. Inside,

Noah, claustrophobic, sat and watched
the occupants of his ark take on
new aspects, shudder into focus one
by one. Something, he thought, must come
of this. Such isolation! Such concentration!
Out of these instinctual half-lit lives
something: some good, some Truth!
That night, a dropped calf bawled to its feet,
shaking off light like dirt.

Noah, an old man, unhappy, shook
his head. Birth was not the answer
nor death. His mind's ark stank
of birth and death, would always,
sundering, stink. Outside,
the fixed demonic patter of rain
saying 'Think, Noah, think! Break this
patter of rain, man!' But only animals
moved in his mind. Now, unbodied by raindrops,
the patter continued, empty, shelled,
clambering down along itself like crabs.
Driven, impotent, he neared despair. Finally,
one bird, uncalled, detached itself,
and battered around inside his skull.

Thankfully, Noah released it, fearful,
hoping, watching it flit and bang
against wind, returning each time,
barren. One day, laden with lies,
it brought back promise of fruit,
of resolution and change.

Now, animals and men crowded the gangplank,
peering eagerly about the returning hills,
for some sign of change. Noah conducted them,
drifting among valleys with breaking smiles,
naming, explaining, directing. Noah, released,
turned once more outwards, giving thanks.

Relief dazed them: nobody realised
nothing had changed. Beast and man
settled and hardened to old moulds, unremembered seasons of death and birth,
led by the bearded one, the prophet, Noah,

rejuvenated, giving thanks on a hill,
moving among known animals and men
with a new aspect, giving thanks; while

leaking, derelict, its mission abandoned,
the ark of his mind wallowed empty westward
to where old rainbows
drown among waves.

Wayne Brown

HAVING EYES THAT SEE

That blind man, at the bus-stop, regularly,
feeling his way along the window's-edge,
turning his palms up, saying, 'Thanks.
God bless you, Ma'am!' and moving on,
until the bus must roar again
and leave him fingering the change
the weary housewife handed him,
breeds like a chigoe in my mind.
And even in a casual magazine,
advertisements assault me for my eyes,
invoke brief passion with their anecdote
of blind girls asking (was this true?),
'Tell me, what colour is the wind?'

The rough compassion, filed away,
returns insisting, now and then,
darkly refusing to be kept unseen,
nagging for close review.

What must I do? Not let the spurious
guilt take charge and lead me groping
to some black idiocy of self-accusing
for having eyes that see. But feelings
prick like Braille and spell
some shadowed vague connection.

Mervyn Morris

A PRETTY POT OF GREY

Three men went to the moon,
and three more isolated a gene.
They're all Americans:
pots of money, lots
of technical skill. Nature's wonders
and defects are a matter of physical conjunctions
and mechanical ignorance.
Know-how and the money to kick it in the arse, onward,
are all it takes for a mole to peer with the eyes of a giant.
The priests can mum their breviary,
and the poets may join the birds;
the Americans will bump and lug, ahead, gathering up
the things they understand. They'll smash
the rest or buy them up.

A gene's a helpless thing: not so difficult to locate,
as lurking Vietcongs, in a giggling
jungle. The highway to the moon
brooks billions, abreast, unlike
the jungles of Vietnam, where obstacles
are man-made and man-met and solved, man
facing man. The poor gene! It's been, there, all
these years, waiting for three Americans
to conquer and isolate it, in the name of politics
and warfare and social peace and Nobel's prize.
And the moon! How long has it been, dear?
And, of course, you couldn't resist! Idly waited

to become a G.I. bride, conquered by chewing-gum,
short-back-top-and-sides and college-boy football
efficiency; Pinkville was a less easy affair, of course.

Human, and its problems need not be faced:
we'll alter man himself (with pills, in spite of Paul
the sixth). So, too, the Nigger peril
can be rinsed away. We'll change their genes, and ask
our allies and the Royal Family to stay
quiet.

Emmanuel Jean-Baptiste

FOR G. W. GORDON

(I)

Poor people!
Starving people!
Naked people!
Black,
downtrodden,
suffering people!
The axe of justice
is at the root of the tree.
Come forth!
Come forth, my people!
Let every voice
shout
so loud that it
cannot be ignored.
Strike back!
Strike back, my people!
Let every blow insist on freedom.

(II)

Those, who withhold relief,
shall sense the bitterness of grief.
The wicked, who exploit the poor,
shall, even as dust on the floor,
be swept in panic on the wind;
then they shall know how they have sinned.
Let us demand our rights of birth,
and assert our claim to this bit of earth.

Here,
we renounce the role
of the wretched
of this earth.
Oh Mother,
dear wife,
you shall be queens
again!
All this and more
shall you inherit,
my son.

Basil Smith

POEM

(1)

Wind-torn banana leaves hang down
and dangle defeated angels'-wings.

The sky is a painted sheath of puffed clouds
in the sunlight.

One breadfruit tree,
with nothing on
but its own bark,
waits for the rain,
and fruit.

In the house,
the smoke of peasant stew, cooking,
curls in the dawn.
The shuffle, inside, is silent,
as the children stare
at their resolute father.

Somebody, their mother, weeps;
but it isn't yesterday's pain;
the tears describe intense fear.

The crop did not come as expected:
poor diet, no fertilizer, no subsidy,
and certain taxes;
a child died, too,
from malnutrition.

And now?

Now, their father downs his tools:
no hoe, no rake, no fork,
no watering can.
No!
Now, he holds the truth
in his hands;
he has joined the Revolution.

(2)
The shoots rise beautifully
in the early showers.

The peasant smiles.

Everything grows, now,
since the *ancien régime* is gone:
the corn,
the wheat,
the rice,
the peas.

The fruits (of labour) hang,
plentiful,
and the pangs of hunger disappear.
The children run up to their parents.
The kiskadee and the dove are satisfied.
The rivers are bountiful
with fish and good water.

The sun shines.
Schools go up.
Clinics, too.
Children don't die.
Music comes from guitars
and loud drums.

The people labour,
and they're productive,
and happy,
after the Revolution.

Michael Als

POEM

(a fragment from
'Memory : Passion : Escape')

To be a child, again.
To be reborn.
To love, again.
To smell fresh-cut sugar cane, again.
To kiss some hidden part of memory.
To wash myself in a West Indian river,
and be baptised, again.
To be me, again.
To be me.

Sebastian Clarke

BLACK HIEROGLYPH

Red on red, rivers of blood flow across the cracked
Earth, I love, filled, as it is, but absorbing
Violence and the voices of fear and the mangled flesh,
    everywhere;
    everything is the bed-rock of my country, and yet they
Ostracise my mother, my woman, and me, from a whole
    Continent,
    and water me down with the Caribbean, catapult me
    to another place, to another time, to another
Love of life, where I am left to die by centuries,
Unshackled by an ocean of sweat, tears, and
Touched only by the cold hands of my dead great-grandfather,
    my sister,
    my father,
    my brother.
    I know they are nameless and numberless.
    The fish have ravaged their proud flesh,
    and the salt of the Atlantic has hardly preserved
    their bones; and yet,
I announce that I am coming from a black thing.
    Beware! Be warned!
Once, a century ago, I screamed, when my mother cried in the
    dark,
    and my father wept with despair.
Now, yes, now, I have come to collect their dues, and mine.
    I am hope.
    I am the Revolution.

I am lighting the light of our fire,
for ever and ever, to see myself by
in the dark.

Tony Matthews

THE COMING

A small slice of sun
illuminates what may, well be, for them,
the final run.

A scratchy, metallic voice
claws the evening air:

'Will all the passengers
for BOAC Flight no. 808,
Kingston to London via New York,
please, board the plane.
Thank you.'

Final hugs. Last kisses.
Unashamed, wet eyes.
Brightly-coloured dresses.
Ill-fitting, new shoes.
Large, Sunday-best trousers,
flapping in the breeze.
Old ladies, shifting corsets
for that little ease.

The engines come to life
with a deafening roar.

Now, only a dot of silver
can be seen, as the huge metal cage swings
high into the sky
towards THE PROMISED, HELPING HAND.

Slowly, we turn away
to Kingston, to face the future
without the ones
in the sky.

We know there's something
coming to take us away, too.

Tony Matthews

FLOWERS

A man I know
wants
to grow;
so, off to Mexico
he goes
for a cactus flower,
and there
marries the cactus plant.

Beginning green,
he soon grows
yellow
with the knowledge
of cactus prickles.

But, the end,
he hopes,
will be mellow
with the wisdom
of his thorns.

                              Claude Lushington

AFTER BEGINNING
(*a poem taken from 'The Mystic Rose'*)

Today I have no first line to start with;
so I'll write down tomorrow's second line
for the day after; then we shall be midway
through the week. Halfway through the seven;
but where is the first of the whole; and how
runs the ink that shapes those words of
unfinished first lines untold? The experience
acquired in between times, however, sustains
the writing even while the ink dries and
lines run out. And why? And wherefore?
And how? are things that do not occur when
there is nothing we do not disown, but accept
all as the abstract of a future unfurled;
halting at colons and commas; gazing over
life's page at a blank, a void, a substance
of time. Is it so requisite then that
we begin it with a first line?

Claude Lushington

Epilogue

LABOURER

Look at his hands,
cactus cracked, pricked,
worn smooth by the hoe,
limestone soil's colour;
he has lost three fingers
of his left hand, falling
asleep at the mill;
the black crushing grin
of the iron tooth'd rachets,
grinding the Guinep Hill cane,
has eaten him lame;
and no one is to blame;

the crunched bone was juicy
to the iron; there was no difference
between his knuckle joints
and ratoon shoots: the soil
receives the liquor cool and sweet;
three fingers are not even worth
a stick of cane; the blood
mix does not show; the star-
gaze crystal sugar shines
no brighter for the cripple blow

and nothing more to show
for thirty years' spine
curving labour in clear
rain, glass-eyed, coming off the sea,
fattening up the mud
in the valleys, cours-
ing down hillsides, causing the toil of the deep,
well-laid roots, gripping soil,
to come steadily loose, junction and joint
between shoot and its flower to be made nonsense of

and the shame, the shame, the shame-
lessness of it all, the nameless days in the burnt cane-
fields without love; crack of its
loud trash, spinn-
ing ashes, wrack of salt odour that will
not free his throat, the cutlass falling, falling, sweat, grit
between fingers, chigga
hatching its sweet nest of pain in his toe;
and now this and now this:
an old man, prickled
to sleep by the weather, his labour,
losing his hands . . .

Edward Brathwaite

CITADEL

From the Pic of Le Cap, where the Citadel sits,
the Arawaks wait;
the flèches of their headdress are stairs up the montagne;

the rings of the palm trees are bells up the montagne;
Toussaint is a zemi;
he stares from the flesh of the stone,

the white of the helmet, Columbus conquistador;
the white of the sword
becomes lightning;

the steel of the cutlass,
the knife of the god;
thongs of the whips

drink water like trees;
Africaines from the slave ships
dance out of the riflemen's loins,

become Dessalines, Dessalines,
La Crête-à-Pierrot,
the spangle of death from the hot

of the trees;
and Christophe Columbus climbs up to his mountain top
with the face of his horse in the faith of his shadow;

he stumbles on a priest, on an African slave, on a Spaniard;
the places of pain become pig snouts;
the black becomes white becomes black becomes rain

falling to plunder the roof
of the world.
Toussaint is a zemi;

he stares from the stone, from the eye-
lids of flame,
at his fate.

Edward Brathwaite

Biographical Notes

MICHAEL ALS Trinidad (1946). Founder-member of The Young Power Movement, Port of Spain, Trinidad and Tobago, a revolutionary group of students and workers. At work on his first book of poems.

ELLIOTT BASTIEN Trinidad (1941). A Chemical Engineer and Petroleum Production expert, now engaged in the Economics of Operational Research at the University of Toronto, Canada. Author of the Essay, 'The Weary Road to Whiteness and the Hasty Retreat into Nationalism' (*Disappointed Guests*, Oxford University Press, 1965).

LOUISE BENNETT Jamaica (1919). A distinguished performing poet and folk satirist, her books include *Anancy Stories and Dialect Verse* (The Pioneer Press, 1957) and *Jamaica Labrish* (Collins and Sangster, 1966).

EDWARD BRATHWAITE Barbados (1930). Lecturer in History at the University of the West Indies, Jamaica, and one of the three editors of *Savacou*, the Journal of the Caribbean Artists' Movement, his outstanding long poems are *Rights of Passage*, *Masks* and *Islands* (Oxford University Press, 1967, 1968 and 1969).

WAYNE BROWN Trinidad (1944). An English Honours graduate of the University of the West Indies, Jamaica (1965–1968), he is at work on his first book of poems.

GEORGE CAMPBELL Jamaica (1918). His *First Poems*, brought out privately in 1945, is among the very few politically-influential early publications of poetry in the Caribbean. He now lives in New York.

H. D. CARBERRY Jamaica (born 1921, Montreal, Canada), Barrister and Bibliophile. Well-known collector of books of Caribbean literature and general publications about the Area. Clerk to the Jamaica Legislature.

243

JAN CAREW   Guyana (1922). Novelist and Visiting Professor of
    Caribbean and Black American Literary Studies at Princeton
    University, New Jersey. His novels include *Black Midas, The Wild
    Coast, The Last Barbarian* (Secker and Warburg, 1958, 1958, 1961)
    and *Cry, Black Power!* (forthcoming). *Moscow is not My Mecca*
    (Secker and Warburg, 1964) is a fictionalised travel report. He
    lives in Toronto, Canada, where he edits *Cotopaxi*, a Review of
    Third World literary and current affairs.

MARTIN CARTER   Guyana (1927). A former political activist in the
    People's Progressive Party, in Georgetown, during the period of
    the liberation struggle under colonialism, and now the Minister of
    Information in the Government of Guyana. Those of his books of
    poetry, published in Georgetown, Guyana, include *The Hill of
    Fire glows Red* (1951), *The Kind Eagle* (1952), and *The Hidden Man*
    (1952). His most influential work is *Poems of Resistance* (Lawrence
    and Wishart Ltd., 1954).

FAUSTIN CHARLES   Trinidad (1944). He came to England, in 1962,
    to study Philosophy at London University, but turned to poetry
    and novel-writing. His first book of poems is *The Expatriate*
    (Brookside Press, 1969).

SEBASTIAN CLARKE   Trinidad (1948). He came to England, when he
    was sixteen. During the first five years, in London, he entered into
    the continuing debate on 'West Indian Identity', in Caribbean
    literary and political groups, and became interested in the cultural
    renaissance coming out of the Black Revolution in America. His
    first book of poems, *Saint and Sinner join in Merriment on the
    Battlefront*, will be published soon in America.

GLORIA ESCOFFERY   Jamaica (1923). Jamaica Scholar, painter and
    one of the poets who contributed to the new literary and artistic
    scene in Jamaica, some years after the politically-definitive riots
    in 1938.

WILSON HARRIS   Guyana (1921). Distinguished novelist and critic.
    Best known for his early book of poems, *Eternity to Season*, which
    he brought out privately in Georgetown, 1954, and, as a novelist,
    for his 'Guyana Quartet', *Palace of the Peacock, The Far Journey
    of Oudin, The Whole Armour* and *The Secret Ladder* (Faber and
    Faber Ltd., 1960, 1961, 1962 and 1963). He has also published
    five other novels, *Heartland, The Eye of the Scarecrow, The
    Waiting Room, Tumatumari* and *Ascent to Omai* (Faber and Faber
    Ltd., 1964, 1965, 1967, 1968 and 1970). *Tradition, the Writer and*

Society (New Beacon Books Ltd., 1967) is his first book of critical essays. He lives in England.

C. L. HERBERT Trinidad (1927). A Grammar School teacher in Port of Spain, Trinidad, and a regular contributor to *Bim*, the leading Caribbean Review of the Arts, and to other literary magazines in America and Canada.

SLADE HOPKINSON Guyana (1934). English and Latin teacher at St. George's College, in Trinidad, and a poet whose work has appeared in most of the literary Reviews and University Journals, throughout the Caribbean. His books are *The Four and Other Poems* (Advocate Publishing Co. Ltd., Barbados, 1954) and *The Onliest Fisherman*, a play (Caribbean Play Series, Extra-Mural Dept., U.C.W.I., 1957).

EMMANUEL JEAN-BAPTISTE Dominica (1939). He came to England, when he was seventeen, won a Scholarship to Oxford University, where he read English, and to the Sorbonne, where he read Philosophy. He taught Latin, English and Philosophy at a private boarding School in Switzerland, and now teaches English language and literature at a Swiss State Gymnasium. Apart from his poetry, he has also written novels, short stories and literary criticism (all in ms.), and has since turned to writing verse drama.

FRANK JOHN Trinidad (1941). Only a few weeks after his arrival in England, in 1967, he began publishing selections of his friends' poems and political speeches, in stapled cyclostyled pamphlets, and distributing them himself, at his own expense. The poems from his ms. of Black Revolutionary verse attracted attention at public readings in London and the Provinces, and have been published in his first collection, *Black Songs* (Longmac Ltd., 1969).

EVAN JONES Jamaica (1926). Former Lecturer in English Literature at Wesleyan University, Philadelphia. Spent a year in Israel with the American Friends Service Committee, doing relief work among Arab refugees, in 1949. Has written *Protector of the Indians*, a Biography of Bartolomé de Las Casas (Nelson, 1958), many television plays for the B.B.C., and scripts for feature films which include those for *The Damned*, *Eve*, *King and Country*, and *Funeral in Berlin*. He lives in England.

RUDOLPH KIZERMAN Barbados (1934). He came to England, in 1952, to study Medicine, became an actor and playwright, and has written a novel, *Stand Up in the World* (Blackbird Books, 1968) and another, in ms., *A Tear for the Strangers*.

KNOLLY S. LA FORTUNE   Trinidad (1920). A Grammar School teacher in London, whose books, brought out privately, include *Moments of Inspiration* (Poetry, Port of Spain, 1946) and *Legend of T-Marie*, A Tale of Trinidad Folklore (Novel, London, 1968).

JOHN LA ROSE   Trinidad (1927). Publisher, radical political activist, during the early Fifties in Port of Spain, and Secretary of the Caribbean Artists' Movement, in London. The list of his publishing house, New Beacon Books Ltd., includes *Foundations* (1966), a book of poems, by John La Rose; *Marcus Garvey, 1887–1940* (1967), a Monograph, by Adolph Edwards; *Tradition, the Writer and Society* (1967), Critical Essays, by Wilson Harris; *Caribbean Writers* (1968), Critical Essays, by Ivan Van Sertima; *New Beacon Reviews, Collection One* (1968), Critical Writing, edited by John La Rose; *Froudacity* (1969), West Indian Fables explained by John Jacob Thomas; *The Theory and Practice of Creole Grammar* (1970), a Linguistic Study of the Creole in Trinidad, by John Jacob Thomas; and *Folk Culture of the Slaves in Jamaica* (1970), a History, by Edward Brathwaite. John La Rose's second book of poems, *Islets of Truth within Me* (1971), is also published by New Beacon Books Ltd.

SYL LOWHAR   Grenada (1935). Although not from Trinidad, he has been adopted by that country, has worked in the Trinidad and Tobago High Commissioner's Office, Georgetown, Guyana, and afterwards studied at the University of the West Indies, Saint Augustine, Trinidad.

CLAUDE LUSHINGTON   Trinidad (1925). Painter and film scriptwriter. He served as a Flight Engineer in the R.A.F., during the last stages of the War. Some years afterwards, he was appointed as one of the Housing Managers in Public Housing in the Government of Trinidad. He returned to England, in 1955, to read Law at the Inner Temple, and has remained on, writing film scripts, painting, and getting together a collection of essays and completing a novel (both in ms.). His first published slim volume of poems is *The Mystic Rose* (Magpie Press, 1969).

MICHAEL ABDUL MALIK   Trinidad (1933) Founder and Chairman of the Racial Adjustment Action Society, and President of the Administration of The Black House, a self-help community project in North London. His poem in this Anthology, 'One Flower', is one of many which the poet has read at Black Power meetings in London and the Provinces, and which has been

246

included in *The Children of Albion*, the Penguin Anthology of Poetry of the 'Underground' in Britain. His assisted autobiography, *From Michael de Freitas to Michael X*, was published by Andre Deutsch Ltd., in 1968.

JAGDIP MARAJ Trinidad (1942). He has written many poems about Trinidad and the Caribbean in which there are noticeable echoes of themes based on the Hindu traditions of the India of his grand-parents who emigrated to Trinidad in the late nineteenth century. His first book of poems, *The Flaming Circle* (McGill Poetry Series No. 10, 1966), was published while he was reading English and Philosophy at McGill University, Montreal, Canada. He has won two major Canadian poetry awards.

TONY MATTHEWS Jamaica (1941). He came to England in 1960, and studied Photography at the Nottinghamshire College of Art, and later became interested in documentary film-making in London. He has written many essays, plays and political articles (all in ms.), and has said that his primary wish is 'to see the Third World Revolution in which *all* the people of the exploited countries will run their own scene, independent of the alien exploiters' super-vision.' He is preparing his first book of poems for publication.

MARINA MAXWELL Trinidad (1934). Lecturer in English and Social Studies at the College of Arts, Science and Technology, Kingston, Jamaica, and Founder of the Yard Theatre, a radical group of actors and writers whose literary and dramatic work aims at achieving urban proletarian participation in the Arts, and Black Revolutionary political education. Her literary articles, political essays and poems appear in the Black radical papers and reviews in the Caribbean and England.

WORDSWORTH MCANDREW Guyana (1936). Journalist and literary critic. His best-known collection of poetry, brought out in George-town, Guyana, is *Blue Gaulding* (Miniature Poets, Series B., 1958).

IAN MCDONALD Trinidad (1933). Novelist. Better known as the poet of two of the most moving Caribbean poems, 'Pineapple Woman' and 'Jaffo, the Calypsonian', he lives in Georgetown, Guyana, where he completed the ms. of his first novel, *The Humming-Bird Tree* (William Heinemann Ltd., 1969).

TONY MCNEILL Jamaica (1941). Awarded the First Prize for Poetry in the Jamaica Festival, 1966, his work is included in *Seven Jamaican Poets* (Bolivar Press, Jamaica, 1971).

JUDY MILES Trinidad (1942). English Honours graduate of the University of the West Indies, Kingston, Jamaica, and student of Psychology at University of British Columbia, Vancouver, Canada, she has contributed poems to all the University journals and literary Reviews in the Caribbean.

MERVYN MORRIS Jamaica (1937). Rhodes Scholar, literary critic, essayist, and Warden of Taylor Hall, University of the West Indies, Kingston, Jamaica, his *Sunday Gleaner* Essay, 'On Reading Louise Bennett Seriously' was awarded the First Prize for the Essay in the Jamaica Festival, 1964; his Essay, 'Feeling, Affection, Respect' (*Disappointed Guests*, edited by Henri Tajfel and John L. Dawson, and published by Oxford University Press, 1965), won the British Institute of Race Relations £100 Prize in 1963–1964; his Literary Essay, 'The Poet as Novelist: The Novels of George Lamming' appeared in *The Islands in Between*, edited by Louis James and published by Oxford University Press, 1968. The poet's essays, literary criticism and poems appear in Caribbean, British Commonwealth and British Anthologies, Reviews, University journals, and newspapers, and his own personal selection of the best of his work is included in *Seven Jamaican Poets* (Bolivar Press, Jamaica, 1971).

ARTHUR RAYMOND Saint Lucia (1947). He came to England, in 1966, to read Law, and, in his own words, he has become 'a former optimist'. He is preparing his first book of poems for publication.

E. M. ROACH Tobago (1915). Former Secondary School teacher, and, now, a literary critic and a staff writer on *The Evening News*, Port of Spain, Trinidad. He writes of himself: 'My whole history is my immediate family, and dimly seen behind the parents, the generations of heavy slave folk trampled into the clay where the sweet cane prospered in our bitter sweat. The poem, 'Homestead', is an artifice of pride: a hut deliberately but not very artfully constructed to shelter my nakedness.'

DENNIS SCOTT Jamaica (1939). Assistant Editor of *Caribbean Quarterly*, a Journal of the University of the West Indies, a radio and television contributor to Arts programmes, an actor-director, and member of the National Dance Theatre Company of Jamaica, his poetry has earned him distinguished national prizes. His *Journey and Ceremonies, Poems: 1960–1969*, brought out privately in Jamaica, in 1969, was a success, and a selection of the best of his work is included in *Seven Jamaican Poets* (Bolivar Press, Jamaica, 1971).

CLIFFORD SEALY Trinidad (1927). After living for many years in England, he returned to Port of Spain, where he now edits *Voices*, a Caribbean literary quarterly, and manages The Book Shop which specialises in Caribbean books, poetry readings and other literary activities. His poems appear in British and Caribbean Anthologies. His most recent publication is *The Professor* (Caribbean Play Series, Extra-Mural Dept., University of the West Indies, Saint Augustine, Trinidad, 1967).

SAMUEL SELVON Trinidad (1923). Novelist and short story writer who began as a poet, and wilfully conceals the fact that he still is one. Since his arrival in England in 1950, he has been awarded two Guggenheim Fellowships, a Society of Authors Travelling Award and a Trinidad Fellowship. His books are internationally well-known. His novels are *A Brighter Sun* (Allan Wingate Ltd., 1952), *An Island is a World* (Allan Wingate Ltd., 1955), *The Lonely Londoners* (Allan Wingate Ltd., 1956), *Ways of Sunlight*, a book of short stories (MacGibbon and Kee Ltd., 1957), *Turn, Again, Tiger* (MacGibbon and Kee Ltd., 1958), *I hear Thunder* (MacGibbon and Kee Ltd., 1963), *The Housing Lark* (MacGibbon and Kee Ltd., 1965), *The Plains of Caroni* (MacGibbon and Kee Ltd., 1970) and two School Readers, *Carnival in Trinidad* (Dept. of Education, New Zealand, 1964) and *A Drink of Water* (Nelson, 1968). He also writes plays for radio and television.

A. J. SEYMOUR Guyana (1914). Founder-Editor of *Kyk-over-al*, the oldest and most influential Guyanese literary Review, and Deputy Chairman of the Guyana National History and Arts Council. His books include *Verse* (Chronicle, 1937), *More Poems* (Chronicle, 1940), *Over Guiana, Clouds* (Standard, 1944), *Suns in my Blood* (Standard, 1944), *Poetry in these Sunny Lands* (Caribia, 1945), *Six Songs* (Caribia, 1946), *The Guiana Book* (Argosy, 1948), and *Leaves from the Tree* (Miniature Poets, Series A, 1951). He has edited *Anthology of West Indian Poetry* (1957) and *Themes of Song* (1961).

BASIL SMITH Jamaica (born Monmouthshire, Wales, 1946). He was taken to Jamaica in 1947, where he was educated, and then came to England, in 1966, to study at the London College of Journalism. In 1968, he took a Diploma Course in the technique of film directing, and returned to Jamaica in 1970. He has experimented, successfully, with the 'multi-voice presentation in poetry-reading', using the poems which he has written, specially, for those experiments, and involving the audiences, dramatically, in the action of the event. His first book of poems is in preparation.

IVAN VAN SERTIMA Guyana (1935). Anthropologist, critic and lecturer on Caribbean writing. He has written *River and the Wall* (Miniature Poets, Series B, 1958) and *Caribbean Writers*, a short, first collection of critical essays (New Beacon Books Ltd., 1968), and compiled the first *Dictionary of Swahili Legal Terms* (University of Dar es Salaam Press, forthcoming). He lives in England.

DEREK WALCOTT Saint Lucia (1930). Journalist, playwright and Founder-Manager of the Trinidad Theatre Workshop (formerly, the Basement Theatre), Port of Spain. His plays, which have been produced in the Caribbean, New York, Toronto, London, Paris and Ibadan, include *Drums and Colours*, a pageant; *Franklin*, a tale of the Islands; *Harry Dernier*, a play for radio; *Henri Christophe*, a chronicle; *Ione*, a play with music; *Malcauchon* or *Six in the Rain*, a one act play; and *The Sea at Dauphin*, *Ti-Jean* and *The Wine of the Country*, all one act plays. His books of poetry are *In a Green Night* (Jonathan Cape Ltd., 1962), *Selected Poems* (Farrar, Straus and Co., New York, 1964), *The Castaway* (Jonathan Cape Ltd., 1965) and *The Gulf and Other Poems* (Jonathan Cape Ltd., 1969). He has been presented with the following awards: a Rockefeller Foundation Fellowship (1957), the Guinness Award for Poetry (1961), the Royal Society of Literature Award (1965), and the Cholmondeley Poetry Award (1969). He lives in Trinidad, his adopted home. He was invited to become Visiting Professor of Commonwealth Literature at Leeds University, 1970 but was unable to do so.

MILTON WILLIAMS Guyana (1936). Regular contributor to *Kyk-over-al*, along with Martin Carter, Wilson Harris, Ivan Van Sertima and Slade Hopkinson. He left Guyana for England shortly after the publication of his first book, *Pray for Rain* (Miniature Poets, Series B, 1958).

Notes

1. The Concealed Spark

Straight Seeking by Tony McNeill   (p. 8)

    Jah Shortened form of Jahveh (Hebrew: *Yah*, *Yahweh*), Jah is the name of God (Jehovah), popularly invoked by the religious group of Rastafarians in Jamaica. The Rastafarians have rejected very nearly all the traditional and contemporary values of Western culture, and believe that the Emperor Haile Selassie I of Ethiopia is the temporal representative of Jah.

Toussaint L'Ouverture by Jan Carew   (p. 11)

    Toussaint L'Ouverture The Haitian revolutionary leader (1743–1803) who liberated the French colony of San Domingo, during the period of the French Revolution, and was overcome by the forces of Bonaparte and transported to France, where he died in the prison fortress of Joux.

The Eye by Jan Carew   (p. 15)

    tinamous South American game-birds, resembling quails, and found in large numbers in the hinterland of Guyana.

The Madwoman of Papine by Slade Hopkinson   (p. 21)

    grampus buses The grampus is a marine mammal which blows and spouts, loudly, and looks like a blunt-headed dolphin. In Jamaica, certain Leyland city buses, whose brakes and doors work, hydraulically, utter similar sounds.

    duppies of dust A duppy (Jamaican vernacular expression) is a spirit of the dead. Hence, the image of ghost-like swirls of dust.

    O / Rass Rass Rass / in the highest Rass is an abusive word of uncertain derivation, used in Jamaican and Guyanese demotic speech. The original name of Emperor Haile Selassie I of Ethiopia, who is venerated by the Rastafarians and many other black

251

Jamaicans, was Ras Tafari, his title, as a young Prince, before his Coronation, in 1930.

Laventville by Derek Walcott   (p. 24)
favelas The shanty settlement of festering slum shacks on the hillsides of Rio de Janeiro, Brazil.

Upside Down Hotel by Elliott Bastien   (p. 28)
Sapodilla The sapodilla plum or naseberry. A small, smooth, brown-skinned, edible fruit.

Evening by Basil Smith   (p. 36)
Rasta Shortened form of Rastafarian. (See Note on Jah). p. 251
chillum pipe (Hindi: *chilam*) The section of a group hookah which contains the burning tobacco. The Rastafarian chillum is made of clay, shaped like a child's straight toy-horn, and held vertically while being smoked.

Poem by John La Rose   (p. 38)
Quashee Sometimes Quashi or Quashie. (Twi word: *Kwasi*, name for a male born on *Kwasida* or *Ayisi's* day, the first day of the week; a day name for a boy born on Sunday.) In Jamaican vernacular usage, a peasant, someone of humble origin, a simple person in the city, or a backward man or woman who refuses improvement. Used, here, by the poet, as a term of endearment.

2. The Heat of Identity

Rimbaud Jingle by Tony McNeill   (p. 61)
lime on stilts Promenade showily.
rock-steady A popular Jamaican urban proletarian dance, during which the two partners stand away from each other defiantly, and pump their arms and legs, barely moving their feet.

Tom Tom by Basil Smith   (p. 73)
abeng (Twi word: *Aben*, animal's horn, musical instrument or tribal ornament.) A cow's horn used as a bugle for signalling by the Jamaican Maroons, within their mountain community of runaway slaves, in the seventeenth and eighteenth centuries.
Shango Yoruba God of thunder.

3. The Fire of Involvement

Homecoming by Dennis Scott   (p. 115)
   higgler's voice (Higgler: an itinerant dealer, market trader of small produce.) The long drawn-out Jamaican vendor's street cry.

The Tightrope Walker by Dennis Scott   (p. 121)
   (For N.W.M.) A poem dedicated to the memory of the former Chief Minister of Jamaica, Norman Washington Manley, who died in 1969.

4. The Blaze of the Struggle

Squatter's rites by Dennis Scott   (p. 151)
   reggae Jamaican urban dance and style of group lyrical expression, made popular, first, among the dissenting young Rastafarians, and later, exploited commercially outside their community.

Saint Ras by Tony McNeill   (p. 158)
   Ras Shortened form of Rastafarian. Also the affectionate prefix for Ras Tafari, the Prince who became Emperor Haile Selassie I of Ethiopia. The poet presents the Rastafarian of his poem as a saintly figure, living in exile within a section of the city, and unaccustomed to the ways of the world, outside his dream of the ideal Ethiopia.

Poem by Edward Brathwaite   (p. 169)
   Akyere (Fante word: female name, *Akyeri*, *Akyere*.) It suggests a specific revelation, and at other times, a very definite kind of vindication of tribal importance.
   sasabonsam Evil spirits.

Haunted Caudillo by Faustin Charles   (p. 187)
   Caudillo Spanish expression for a leader with great power. Now used in Latin American countries to describe a person whose leadership is personal and undemocratic.

5. Breaklight

Having Eyes that See by Mervyn Morris   (p. 221)
   chigoe A flea which burrows into the skin, and causes inflammation and painful swelling, usually in the feet of peasants and country-people who often go about barefooted.

Citadel by Edward Brathwaite   (p. 241)

    zemi A noble spirit, in the pantheon of Haitian Voodoo loa, who inhabits the rocks and hillsides of mountains.

    Dessalines Emperor Jean-Jacques Dessalines I of Haiti (1758–1806). Founder of the Haitian State in 1804, he began as one of the three celebrated revolutionary leaders (the others were Toussaint L'Ouverture and Henri Christophe) who fought for the Independence of Haiti from the French. He ruled as Emperor from 1804 to 1806.

    La Crête-à-Pierrot Toussaint L'Ouverture had his fortune told in the Haitian fort of La Crête-à-Pierrot by an itinerant hounghan (a Voodoo priest) who prophesied that Toussaint would be betrayed and handed over to the French by his trusted and senior General Dessalines.

Acknowledgements

The Editor and Publishers are grateful to the following copyright holders for permission to include copyright material in this anthology, and for information about sources:

For MICHAEL ALS: 'Pain' and 'Poem'; to the Author.

For ELLIOTT BASTIEN: 'Upside Down Hotel'; to the Author.

For LOUISE BENNETT: 'Colonisation in Reverse' from *Jamaica Labrish* published by Collins and Sangster Ltd., Jamaica; to the Author.

For EDWARD BRATHWAITE: 'Citadel', 'Labourer'; to the Author; 'Ogun' (from *Islands*), 'Poem' (from *Masks*), 'Poem', 'Poem', 'South' and 'The Spade' (from *Rights of Passage*); to the Author and Oxford University Press.

For WAYNE BROWN: 'Devilfish', 'Famine', 'Fisherman's Song', 'Rasta Fisherman', 'Red Hills', 'Soul on Ice' and 'Tiger'; to the Author; also to the Author for 'Noah' (first published in *Jamaica Journal*), and 'Squid' (first published in *Link*, a St. Lucian literary magazine).

For GEORGE CAMPBELL: 'History Makers', first published in the magazine *Focus*, Jamaica; to the Author.

For H. D. CARBERRY: 'Poem', first published in the magazine *Focus*, Jamaica; to the Author.

For JAN CAREW: 'Ten Years: 1959–1969', 'The Eye' and 'Toussaint L'Ouverture'; to the Author.

For MARTIN CARTER: 'Cartman of Dayclean', 'Death of a Comrade', 'I clench my fist', 'I come from the Nigger Yard', 'This is the dark time, my love' and 'On the Fourth Night of a Hunger Strike', all from *Poems of Resistance*; to the Author and Lawrence and Wishart Ltd., London; also to the Author for 'Looking at your Hands', 'Poems of Shape and Motion', 'Voices' and 'You are Involved', from *Kyk-over-al* magazine, Guyana.

For FAUSTIN CHARLES: 'A Dedication to Cuba', 'Calypsonian', 'Soucouyant', 'Sugar Cane' and 'Sugar Cane Man'; to the Author; also to the Author for 'Haunted Caudillo', first published in *Caribbean Artists' Movement Newsletter No. 2.*

For SEBASTIAN CLARKE: 'Child-Mother in Metamorphosis', 'Poem' and 'Poem' from *Saint and Sinner Join in Merriment on Battle Front*; to the Author.

For GLORIA ESCOFFERY: 'Guyanese Reflections', first published in the magazine, *Bim*, Barbados; to the Author.

For WILSON HARRIS: 'Sun Poem XV', first published in the magazine *Kyk-over-al*, Guyana; to the Author.

For C. L. HERBERT: 'Poem'; to the Author.

For SLADE HOPKINSON: 'The Madwoman of Papine', first published in the magazine *Bim*, Barbados; to the Author.

For EMMANUEL JEAN-BAPTISTE: 'A pretty pot of grey' and 'Speaking Twice'; to the Author.

For FRANK JOHN: 'Husa' and 'Poem'; to the Author; also to the Author for 'No Joke', first published in *Black Songs*, Longmac, London.

For EVAN JONES: 'The Song of the Banana Man', first published in the magazine *Bim*, Barbados; to the Author and Christopher Mann Ltd., London.

For RUDOLPH KIZERMAN: 'The Invisible'; to the Author and Murray Pollinger Ltd., London.

For KNOLLY S. LA FORTUNE: 'Breaklight'; to the Author.

For JOHN LA ROSE: 'Not from Here' and 'Their Bullring' from *Foundations*, and 'Poem' and 'Prose Poem for a Conference' from *Islets of Truth Within Me*; to the Author and New Beacon Books Ltd., London.

For SYL LOWHAR: 'The Colonial', first published in *New World Quarterly* edited by George Lamming; to the Author.

For CLAUDE LUSHINGTON: 'A Christmas Banquet', 'A Pound of Flesh at Market Price', 'Eleventh Hour', 'Flowers', 'Hurricane' and 'Simon: How many Bolivars?'; to the Author; also to the Author for 'After Beginning', first published in *The Mystic Rose*, Magpie Press, London.

For MICHAEL ABDUL MALIK: 'One Flower'; to the Author.

For JAGDIP MARAJ: 'Faded Beauty' and 'The Flaming Circle', from *The Flaming Circle*, McGill University, Canada; to the Author.

For TONY MATTHEWS: 'Black Hieroglyph', 'Blues', 'Song of Dry Bones' and 'The Coming'; to the Author.

For MARINA MAXWELL: 'For Denis who was a Drum'; to the Author.

For WORDSWORTH MCANDREW: 'Blue Gaulding' and 'Legend of the Carrion Crow'; to the Author.

For IAN MCDONALD: 'Jaffo, the calypsonian', first published in the magazine, *Bim*, Barbados; to the Author.

For TONY MCNEILL: 'Iris', 'Ode to Brother Joe', '1-2', 'Residue',

'Rimbaud Jingle', 'Saint Ras', 'Spring Poem: Brown's Town', 'Straight Seeking', 'The Children', 'The Crack', 'The Other Side of the Mummies' and 'Who'll see me dive?'; to the Author. Most of these poems have been previously published in *Jamaica Journal* and *The Sunday Gleaner*.

For JUDY MILES: 'Suicide?' from *Voices* magazine, edited by Clifford Sealy, Trinidad and Tobago; to the Author.

For MERVYN MORRIS: 'Having Eyes that See', 'Mariners', 'The Early Rebels', 'The Poets' and 'The Pond', all of which (except 'Mariners') were first published in the magazine *Bim*, edited by Frank Collymore, Barbados; and 'Valley Prince', first published in *Jamaica Journal*, edited by Alex Gradussov, Jamaica; to the Author.

For ARTHUR RAYMOND: 'A Revolutionary Core: Che Guevara' and 'On the Bright Side'; to the Author.

For E. M. ROACH: 'Homestead'; to the Author.

For DENNIS SCOTT: 'A Kind of Karate', 'Cortege', 'Club', 'Epitaph', 'Exile', 'Fisherman', 'Homecoming', 'Infidelities', 'Resurrections', 'Squatter's Rites', 'The Tightrope Walker', 'Uncle Time' and 'Visionary'; to the Author.

For CLIFFORD SEALY: 'Birth of a Nation', first published in *Voices*, Trinidad and Tobago; to the Author.

For SAMUEL SELVON: 'Variation', first published in the magazine *Bim*, Barbados; to the Author.

For A. J. SEYMOUR: 'The Sun is a Shapely Fire', first published in *Kyk-over-al*, edited by A. J. Seymour, Guyana; to the Author.

For BASIL SMITH: 'And Away', 'Evening', 'For G. W. Gordon', 'My Heritage', 'The Intruder', 'This Land' and 'Tom Tom'; to the Author.

For IVAN VAN SERTIMA: 'Volcano', first published in *Kyk-over-al*, Guyana, and 'Menagerie'; to the Author.

For DEREK WALCOTT: 'The Survey', which is the first part of *Guyana*, taken from *The Gulf*; 'Exile', 'Che', 'Poem' and 'Negatives', all from *The Gulf*; and 'Laventville' from *The Castaway*; to the Author, to Jonathan Cape Ltd., London, and to Farrar, Straus & Giroux, Inc., New York.

For MILTON WILLIAMS: 'At the Moment', 'Iron punts laden with cane' and 'Pray for Rain', all first published in *Kyk-over-al*, Guyana; to the Author.

The Editor and Publishers have made every effort to trace the holders of copyright in all poems included in this Anthology. If, however, any query should arise, it should be addressed to the Publishers, and if it is found that an error has inadvertently been made it will be corrected in any future editions of the book.

Index of Poets and Titles

ALS, Michael
  Pain 39
  Poem 226

BASTIEN, Elliott
  Upside Down Hotel 28
BENNETT, Louise
  Colonisation in Reverse 51
BRATHWAITE, Edward
  Citadel 241
  Labourer 239
  Ogun 48
  Poem 169
  Poem 212
  Poem 215
  South 46
  The Spade 43
BROWN, Wayne
  Devilfish 161
  Famine 17
  Fisherman's Song 18
  Noah 218
  Rasta Fisherman 70
  Red Hills 20
  Soul on Ice 128
  Squid 126
  Tiger 68

CAMPBELL, George
  History Makers 33
CARBERRY, H. D.
  Poem 142
CAREW, Jan
  Ten Years: 1959–1969 189

The Eye   15
Toussaint L'Ouverture   11
CARTER, Martin
  Cartman of Dayclean   165
  Death of a Comrade   163
  I clench my fist   166
  I come from the Nigger Yard   96
  Looking at your hands   134
  On the Fourth Night of a Hunger Strike   167
  Poems of Shape and Motion   136
  This is the dark time, my love   16
  Voices   133
  You are Involved   135
CHARLES, Faustin
  A Dedication to Cuba   130
  Calypsonian   91
  Haunted Caudillo   187
  Soucouyant   131
  Sugar Cane   185
  Sugar Cane Man   88
CLARKE, Sebastian
  Child-Mother in Metamorphosis   32
  Poem   105
  Poem   229

ESCOFFERY, Gloria
  Guyanese Reflections   95

HARRIS, Wilson
  Sun Poem XV   85
HERBERT, C. L.
  Poem   37
HOPKINSON, Slade
  The Madwoman of Papine   21

JEAN-BAPTISTE, Emmanuel
  A pretty pot of grey   222
  Speaking Twice   141
JOHN, Frank
  Husa   108
  No Joke   143
  Poem   168
JONES, Evan
  The Song of the Banana Man   101

KIZERMAN, Rudolph
  The Invisible   107

LA FORTUNE, Knollys
  Breaklight 199
LA ROSE, John
  Not from Here 76
  Poem 38
  Prose Poem for a Conference 74
  Their Bullring 78
LOWHAR, Syl
  The Colonial 79
LUSHINGTON, Claude
  A Christmas Banquet 53
  A Pound of Flesh at Market Price 147
  After Beginning 235
  Eleventh Hour 148
  Flowers 234
  Hurricane 110
  Simon: How many Bolivars? 194

MALIK, Michael Abdul
  One Flower 146
MARAJ, Jagdip
  Faded Beauty 87
  The Flaming Circle 86
MATTHEWS, Tony
  Black Hieroglyph 230
  Blues 94
  Song of Dry Bones 92
  The Coming 232
MAXWELL, Marina
  For Denis who was a Drum 172
MCANDREW, Wordsworth
  Blue Gaulding 31
  Legend of the Carrion Crow 80
MCDONALD, Ian
  Jaffo, the calypsonian 34
MCNEILL, Tony
  Blue Sunday 5
  Iris 6
  Ode to Brother Joe 154
  1–2 156
  Residue 60
  Rimbaud Jingle 61
  Saint Ras 158
  Spring Poem: Brown's Town 209
  Straight Seeking 8
  The Children 211
  The Crack 207

The Other Side of the Mummies   208
Who'll see me dive?   123
MILES, Judy
   Suicide?   178
MORRIS, Mervyn
   Having Eyes that See   221
   Mariners   160
   The Early Rebels   9
   The Poets   10
   The Pond   63
   Valley Prince   125

RAYMOND, Arthur
   A Revolutionary Core: Che Guevara   184
   On the Bright Side   104
ROACH, E. M.
   Homestead   98

SCOTT, Dennis
   A Kind of Karate   117
   Cortege   203
   Cub   119
   Epitaph   4
   Exile   59
   Fisherman   201
   Homecoming   115
   Infidelities   3
   Resurrections   205
   Squatter's Rites   151
   The Tightrope Walker   121
   Uncle Time   153
   Visionary   202
SEALY, Clifford
   Birth of a Nation   29
SELVON, Samuel
   Variation   145
SEYMOUR, A. J.
   The Sun is a Shapely Fire   82
SMITH, Basil
   And Away   72
   Evening   36
   For G. W. Gordon   224
   My Heritage   71
   The Intruder   140
   This Land   175
   Tom Tom   73

VAN SERTIMA, Ivan
  Menagerie 40
  Volcano 41

WALCOTT, Derek
  Che 182
  Exile 64
  Laventville 24
  Negatives 183
  Poem 67
  The Survey 217
WILLIAMS, Milton
  At the Moment 106
  Iron punts laden with cane 30
  Pray for Rain 180

Index of First Lines

A blues in the night   94
A man I know   234
A newsclip: the invasion of Biafra   183
A small slice of sun   232
Among the clouds   130

Behind a green tree the whole sky is dying   133
Blue is the journey I long to go   85
Breaklight   199
But today I recaptured the islands'   46

Could these soft huts   169

Damn Caliban!   38
Death must not find us thinking that we die   163

Every stance seemed crooked. He had   158
Everywhere Fish wheeled and fled   218

Fat butterfly, fleshed in sin   161
For tomorrow, the woods   215
Four years ago   21
From the hollowness of the cave   79
From the jetty's crusted edge   18
From the Pic of Le Cap, where the Citadel sits   241

Give me tickets for innocence   148
Give me tom-tom   73
Green leaves   32

Hear me boast, *bai*, brother   95
Here are only the wind and two waters   37
Here's an animal   119
His glass eye's in   6
Hyphen-stretched, between Mustang and mule   20

I am wired for sound. I live 156
I' beatin' me husa drum 108
I have not eaten for four days 167
I haven't come to conquer 140
I live in a mammoth menagerie 40
I realise now that 72
I speak, today 189
I want to shape you on the anvil of my will 147
I was wondering if I could shape this passion 136
In seasons of drought 180
In this dark-grained news-photograph, whose glare 182
Instantly, the horizon tilts and whirls 128
Iron punts, laden with cane 30
It huddled there 24
It takes a mighty fire 142

Jaffo was a great calypsonian 34

Later, they said that 121
Look at his hands 239

Many believe, one day, the ship 8
Me one, way out in the crowd 125
My choir and your choir 92
My 'fore-day morning dream lingers 15
My heritage is of the night 71
My uncle made chairs, tables, balanced doors on, dug out 48

No! 134
No more damn' nonsense 143
Nothing can soak 154
Now, to begin the road 165

Old Rasta, how that rumpled bark becomes you still 70
On Sunday, all come to the zoo 61
One great wing marks his shoulder 202
One spark 184
One swings up- 211

Peas, corn, potatoes; he had 151
Pinned to the clothes-line of time to dry 53
Poor people! 224

Red on red, rivers of blood flow across the cracked 230

Sancho, any Sancho 187
scorched 212
Seaweeds 178

Seven splendid cedars break the trades   98
Severed by mercenary fate   87
Simon: How many Bolivars?   194
Sometimes, I marvel at my perfection   104
Stilts support the silent, slate-blue   31
Strangled in the womb   29
Suffering   78
Sun, sea, shady mango groves, and   175
Sunday evening. Memories stain   5

Tall, with slow   43
That blind man, at the bus-stop, regularly   221
The air shone like glass   209
The bee-like hum, in the ears   208
The old colonial steamship   126
The pain   39
The Rasta sits in an island   36
The scales, like metal, flint his feet   201
The succulent flower bleeds molasses   185
The sun is a shapely fire   82
The sun's no friend of mine, who grew up   68
The surveyor straightens from his theodolite   217
The tourists peel off their dollars   28
The wind is crisp, and carries   60
The wind is making countries   115
The window saw   110
Their grief's-wind blows him   203
There is a kind of loss   59
There's nothing delicate   205
There was a famine on the waterfront   17
There was this pond in the village   63
They call you Carrion Crow   80
They don't even know   107
They hanged him on a clement morning, swung   4
This I have learned   135
This is the dark time, my love   16
Three men went to the moon   222
Time and the changing passions played them tricks   9
To be a child, again   229
To be exiled   106
Today I have no first line to start with   235
Today, I thought I glimpsed death   207
Touris', white man, wipin' his face   101
Towards that flaming circle   86
Two boys battle on a flat, green field   3

Uncle Time is a ol', ol' man   153

Until today, in the middle of the tumult   96

Wat a joyful news, Miss Mattie!   51
We're a people of exile, living in the permanence of tragedy   74
What can we do   172
What is it? I wonder   168
When I, no longer, pretended   117
When I speak, now   41
When unseen strangers lounge beyond the footlights   10
Where I'm at! Where you're at!   105
While men watched the cities disintegrating   146
Who am I   88
who are   160
'Who is slave and who is free   11
Who'll see me dive? Look! here am I   123
Whose world was shell was his, which stood   145
Wind-haired, mufflered   64
Wind-torn banana leaves hang down   226
Witch of flying fire   131
Women stone breakers   33

Yet the South felt like home. Wrought balconies   67
You chime sweet sounds   91
You come, in warships, terrible with death   166
You know, if I were to tell you that I love you   141
You were not born, here   76